MW00635766

Imagining Maine
Essays and Stories

Warmest regards,

Allan Lockyer

2007

Cover "The Willows" Steuben, Maine, January 1967
Photo by Author

"Playing in the Willows" Steuben 1967
Ronnie Parritt and the Smeal brothers
Photo by Author

Imagining Maine
Essays and Stories

by Allan Lockyer

Published 2004 by Berry Cove Publishing Company,
17 Kitts Crossing, Lamoine, Maine 04605

Imagining Maine - Essays and Stories
Copyright © 2004 by Allan Lockyer

Berry Cove Publishing Company,
17 Kitts Crossing, Lamoine, Maine 04605
tom@berrycovepublishing.com

ISBN 0-9722679-1-3

Library of Congress Catalog Card Number: 2004104399

In Loving Memory
Of My Mother
GLADYS LOCKYER
2 February 1915 Irvington, New Jersey
4 May 2003 Califon, New Jersey

Acknowledgements

The author wishes to thank Phyllis Driggers, Fred and Nancy Hastings, Linda Lockyer, Bill Ramsey, and Tom and Sharon St. Claire.

Table of Contents

Part Two

<u>Stories</u>

PROLOGUE

As far back as I can remember, I've wanted to live in Maine. My parents took me there on vacations when I was a child. And then in 1959, when I was eight, they bought an old farmhouse way Downeast in Steuben. We went there on vacations until my father died in 1966. Later that summer, my mother decided to sell our family home in New Jersey, and she and I moved to the old house in Steuben. I was enrolled as a sophomore at Sumner Memorial High School in East Sullivan. It was surely the worst year of my life. Not only did I miss my father terribly, and the boyhood friends and relatives I left behind, but the Maine I discovered at Sumner High School was nothing like what I had imagined. I'm not sure what I had imagined. Sumner had its cliques and its "in" crowd, and to my amazement, basketball, a sport I had never played, was almost like the school's religion. Basketball? I never would have associated it with Maine. I guess I had always imagined Maine as an outdoorsy sort of place where people skied or else played ice hockey on the lakes and ponds. Never in my wildest dreams could I have imagined Maine kids cooped up all winter in gymnasiums bouncing round balls.

Over time, I slowly made friends and adjusted to the basketball-crazed culture of Sumner High. The other Maine—the woods, bays, lakes, and ponds—I immediately embraced. I've always loved being outdoors in any sort of weather and I quickly adjusted to life in the tiny village of Steuben. I didn't miss anything about New Jersey, especially its affluent culture. I never felt like I belonged there anyway. I especially liked the directness, honesty, and unpretentiousness of the people Downeast, and in time I grew to really like my classmates, many of whom I still see every summer.

As I write this introduction, I'm sitting in my office on an August afternoon in Florence, South Carolina. The circuitous path I traveled to wind up here is revealed in bits and pieces in the essays and stories that follow. I guess I'm a frustrated Mainer in exile as I've lived in eight other states besides Maine since graduating from Sumner in 1969. It was never my intention to leave Maine permanently when I went away to college, but I've taken what opportunities life has offered, and it has brought me mostly joy. Still, I'm sitting here daydreaming about Jones Pond in West Gouldsboro, the one place on earth I've most wanted to be since I was fifteen. Meanwhile, outside my office window the heat index is approaching 110 degrees. In a few hours I'll be jogging slow laps around a shaded park in Marion, the South Carolina town where I've lived since 1986. But at this very moment, my eyes are fixating on a map of Maine on my office wall. I'm looking intently at the Gouldsboro Peninsula across Frenchman Bay from Bar Harbor. I'm trying to imagine our camp at this very moment. What I'd give to be there now!

IMAGINING MAINE is an eclectic mix of essays and stories written over the past decade and a half. For me, writing essays and stories has served as a relief valve from my career as a college professor. Writing, along with long distance running, has been my way of putting things into perspective, to keep from falling into that "career obsession" that so many academics and other professionals get caught up in, where one's position and accomplishments as a scholar become one's identity. Maybe I'm foolish or naïve, but my career has never been a priority with me. And at this point in my life, I'm more concerned with my spiritual health. It seems to me, that by the time we get into our fifties, we need to stand back, take stock, and decide what really matters. My life is more than half over. Actually, I stopped worrying about my career shortly after getting out of graduate school. I realized then that I'd much rather write for a larger audience than a tiny number of scholars.

My focus in this collection is on places: Maine and South Carolina, where I live and work; and Mexico and Ireland, two other countries I've been drawn to. For a geographer, I really haven't been much of a traveler. I'm not sure I even like to travel. Indeed, I've been a most reluctant traveler. Partly it has been due to a lack of money; but mostly it comes from a reluctance to leave home. And if I can't bring my dog along, then I almost need a bomb placed under me to get out of the house. There's also quite a bit of Thoreau in me, in that I'm more concerned with the local than with the wider world.

Although I've lived in nine states, including Maine, since 1969, our camp on Jones Pond in West Gouldsboro has been home base. I've spent summers there since 1973, so you might say I've lived part of my life in Maine. I like to tell people that I work in South Carolina, but live in Maine. But can someone who passes the long winter outside the state call oneself a Mainer? I doubt it. My heart may be in Maine, but I'm merely a summer resident who dreams about life Downeast the rest of the year. The Maine that I write about is the Maine that I imagine. Indeed, my view of Maine is probably quite different from the views of native Maine writers like Carolyn Chute, John Gould, Stephen King, Cathy Pelletier, Sanford Phippen, or Carroll Terrell.

Still, I'm very protective of my Maine; I suppose, because I only get to live there from mid-May through early August. I get upset when I imagine my Maine threatened by cultural or environmental change. I'm extremely territorial; I'm especially troubled by development. I'm a no-growth person. A new subdivision cut through a swath of forest to the coastline is like a deep wound in my flesh. The Maine that I imagine is my refuge from the Florida-like cancer that has consumed most of the East Coast. At times, I just want to be fog-bound, with only the sounds of the birds, frogs, and loons. Ideally, I want everything in Maine to stay the same as it was when I first laid eyes on it in the 1950s. Sometimes I think I'm actually happier in South Carolina...because I don't love that state enough to get upset by its on-going development. Mine is a romantic image of Maine—more dream-like than reality. But for me, dreaming about Maine gets me through the other nine months.

I began writing occasional essays and stories and sending them to *The Downeast Coastal Press,* a weekly newspaper based in Cutler, soon after its inception in 1988. I was then at a crossroads in my career. I had recently completed a doctoral degree and was doing the requisite things— writing scholarly papers and presenting them at professional conferences—needed to secure tenure at a university. But I also began to realize that I simply enjoyed writing—not the tortured, deadly sort of prose published in scholarly journals, but a more lively, whimsical type of expression accessible to the general public. The *DCP* was one of the first venues that made this possible for me, and I'm extremely grateful to them for allowing me space all these years. Some of the essays and stories were later published in other publications, while the longer essays included here were previously unpublished.

The essays are arranged in chronological order beginning in 1990 and ending in 2003. The stories have been reworked and labored over so much that I've not given them a specific date. These essays and stories reflect my interests and travels during this period. Some of them may come as surprises in a book with the title *IMAGINING MAINE*, but there are threads that tie them to the book's overall themes. For example, I included "The Day of the Dead" because it is an in-depth look at Michoacán, the Mexican state that sends more than half of its population to live and work in the United States. In Milbridge, Maine, approximately ten percent of the town's residents are immigrants from Mexico or Central America, some from Michoacán. Who are these people? What sort of culture and environment do they hail from? I traveled there nearly a dozen times between 1991 and 2003, and some of what I discovered is revealed in "The Day of the Dead."

In the process of writing these essays I began to search my soul for answers to that timeless question: Who am I? Or, what am I? Am I a scholar, a teacher, a writer, or just a witness? This inner conflict between scholar and writer, and social scientist and humanist, seems to work itself out as the years go by and the essays pile up. Indeed, middle-age has come as a welcome reprieve from the harried pace of my younger years, when I was trying to complete my formal education and establish myself in a career. I've always been a daydreamer, and writing has been, for me, a form of meditation as soothing as music or prayer.

Allan Lockyer
August 2003

COUNTRY STORES IN SOUTH CAROLINA AND MAINE

The first sounds I would hear were the chirps of crickets. Not crickets in the wild; crickets in captivity — in a big wooden bin in front of the country store. It was May, and I was driving slowly along flat country roads, past sun-scorched fields of young tobacco plants, in the Pee Dee region of South Carolina's coastal plain. Gasoline was still cheap; I had finished teaching spring semester; and I was free to stop at country stores — tiny mom and pop establishments along the highway or at rural crossroads — to look around a bit, maybe drink a bottle of soda, and talk to locals about fishing.

In June, when my wife had finished teaching school, we'd go back to Maine, to our cabin in the woods, without electricity, indoor plumbing, or supermarkets nearby. We would rely on local country stores for many necessities, and then I would see how similar, or how different, rural stores in Maine and South Carolina really are.

Carolina country stores tend to be older, dirtier, and more authentic than the ones Down East in Maine. You won't find many college-educated out-of-staters, yuppies, or exiles from suburbia behind the counters of genuine Carolina country stores. Indeed, most rural Carolina store owners have never left the land. This is strictly local stuff: feed, seed, chewing tobacco, snuff, cane fishing poles, crickets, worms, old fashioned hoop cheese and crackers, two-dollar six-packs, and pot-bellied woodstoves. You can buy a "Brim-Buster" adjustable-length fishing rod and all the bait and tackle you'll ever need, but no gourmet foods, fancy French wines, or Brie cheese.

But Maine is very "in" these days — and not just Kennebunkport. It's the ex-urban migration from places already overcrowded; it's the last "frontier" of the East; it's this perception that life is simpler, freer, and still worth living in Maine. Whatever the reason, you're just as likely to find an out-of-stater as you are a native Downeaster behind the counter of a typical Maine country store. The out-of-staters are here to get out of the "rat race," but they're bringing bits of suburbia with them. Indeed, they're slowly changing the character of Maine's country stores.

It's not the same store; the ambience is gone; the newcomers don't understand the local customs or the locals who have loitered in that same corner of the building for a couple-three generations. And most newcomers will not give you credit. They can't afford to. Unlike native Maine store owners, the out-of-staters mortgage, rather than inherit their store buildings. Consequently, they've got more to lose; and, they may not even know that credit is the mark of a true country store. Years ago, you could always "set it down" until times got better. (And this was — and still is — so important in Maine where winters are long and so many jobs are seasonal.) But not any more. In Maine, these days, you can expect to encounter a CASH ONLY, NO CREDIT! sign on most store counters.

But in the Pee Dee region of South Carolina, most country stores cannot survive without giving credit. Farmers expect it, and so does everyone else. Of course, the proprietors have to know their customers; or, at least they have to know how to deal with them. One store owner told me: "You need to stay right on top of your customers. You need to make sure they keep coming back. It's not the competition that matters; it's how you treat your customers...to win their loyalty." The proprietor told me that a black man owed him a lot on his bill. He told the black man that he was more concerned about keeping his (the black man's) business than he was about his unpaid bill. He said the black man turned around and bought several dollars worth of groceries after that. The proprietor smiled; then in a low voice, scarcely above a whisper, he said: "Black folks can drive you crazy, but they'll spend every dollar they've got."

The racial issue is always present in South Carolina. And subtleties regarding race are often evident in Carolina country stores. This is the old South, after all, and attitudes have been slow to change. Most rural stores are owned by whites; although many stores are in predominantly black communities. I found very few — only two out of fifty that I visited — that were black-owned. Despite the patronizing attitudes of some whites towards blacks — and these whites often fail to see themselves as patronizing — the races do seem to get along fine.

And Southern country stores are good places to observe and learn about race relations. Unlike the Northeastern United States, where blacks and whites seem to fear and distrust one another, there is a greater understanding of the respective cultures in the South. The view I got from country stores was of two races that have lived side by side for generations, albeit maintaining a certain measure of social distance and mutual respect. Admittedly, simply hanging around the local country stores may not provide a "scientific" methodology by which to measure race relations, but it does give one a "feel" for the way things are.

In Maine, the country store gossip is as likely to be about out-of-staters as about Mainers themselves. Out-of-staters are buying up more and more of Maine's coastline — besides its country stores — making it harder for local clam and marine worm diggers to get down to the mudflats. They're also driving up the price of real estate, which makes it hard for Downeasters, who struggle all year in the local resource industries — clamming, fishing, logging, wreath-making, and blueberry raking — to afford anything but mobile homes. Indeed, much of what I know about the harsh realities of eastern Maine's marginal economy, I got at country stores. As one proprietor told me: "If I haven't heard it, it hasn't happened. They get around to discussing it all before the day's over." Another store owner said: "You can hear anything you want to hear, like who are going to have babies and who aren't."

In both states, country stores are great places to learn about the local people and culture. And after visiting country stores in Maine, South Carolina, and several states in between, I'm convinced that the number one reason patrons stop is not to buy something, but rather to talk to friends and neighbors. "They just stop in for something to do," a proprietor in Maine told me. "Most of my customers stop two or three times a day."

But even if you don't want to talk to people, you can learn a lot just from reading the notices on the doors, walls, and windows of country stores. Here are things I read last summer in Maine:

"Unattended children will be sold as slaves."

"Blueberry rakers wanted."

"Mulch for sale."

"Taylor's worms and crawlers."

"Gossip welcomed here."

"As soon as the rush is over, I'm going to have a nervous breakdown. I owe it to myself. I worked for it and nobody is going to deprive me of it."

And, in South Carolina, I read:

"This store is guarded by a PIT BULL with AIDS."

"To our past due customers, when you DIE, please let us be your PALLBEARERS. We carried you so long that we would like to finish the job!"

"No bad boys allowed. Be good or be gone."

"Wanted: Good woman who can sew, clean fish, dig worms, and has boat and motor and deer dogs. Send photo of boat and motor and deer dogs."

There have been many changes in country stores over the years. One of the most obvious is the emphasis now on fast foods — hot sandwiches, pizza, even fried chicken — and convenience. In both Maine and South Carolina, little mom and pop country stores are mimicking the franchised convenience chains. Gone from most stores are the bulk items, the overalls, boots, and shoes; the old cork-lined "drink boxes" (coolers) are being replaced by modern upright "walk-in" coolers. Home deliveries are just about gone; in-store service is disappearing also; it's get your own stuff and go!

In Maine, country stores have acquired a new function in recent years — as gambling casinos. A Megabucks state lottery machine is likely to be displayed prominently on the counter, alongside the Italian (submarine) sandwiches, the Slim Jims, and the dried "strip" Codfish. Clam diggers stop after a morning on the mudflats, their hip rubber boots tracking in gray-black muck, to cash their checks, grab some lunch, maybe a twelve-pack, two or three dollars worth of "scratch-offs," or a Megabucks lottery ticket.

But who knows? Perhaps they'll get lucky like the twenty-seven-year-old man in Jonesport who won a seven million dollar jackpot a couple of years ago. "Everybody's a gambler down here," a store owner in South Addison told me. "That's about all people do in the winter. They dig clams, gamble, and they starve."

Gambling is not legal in South Carolina country stores, but I've been told it goes on behind the scenes in some stores. (South Carolina now has the Education Lottery and the machines are now appearing in convenience stores.) Most country stores, North or South, are pretty tame places. If they're too rowdy, or if they are perceived as unsafe or uninviting, they tend to lose their most important customers — women. Whereas men are responsible for much of the loitering in rural stores, women do the serious shopping. One store owner in Maine told me he purposely removed the lunch counter, despite the protests of the local men who habitually loitered there drinking coffee hours on end. Evidently, the women in the community had felt uncomfortable walking past the counter of unkempt men and had gradually stopped patronizing his store. "A car would pull up, the man would get out but the women refused to cross the threshold," he explained. "So I took out the lunch counter and the women came back."

Perhaps the biggest "vice" associated with country stores in both Maine and South Carolina is the sale and consumption of alcoholic beverages. In both states, it is possible to purchase beer or wine at a country store. And as country stores have phased out their clothing, hardware, bulk items, and groceries, and made the transition from general merchandise to convenience stores, they have increasingly become rural beer depots.

In both states, I have noticed that the older generation of store proprietors — let's say those that were born before the second World War — are less likely to sell alcoholic beverages than the younger generation. And in South Carolina, where the overall population density is about twice that

of Maine, and where there are, understandably, far more surviving country stores, I encountered many proprietors who simply refused to sell beer
or wine. After all, South Carolina is part of the "Bible Belt." Indeed,
when I asked one elderly proprietor how his family had survived in the
store business the past one hundred years, he said: "We are believers in
God!"

The decision to sell alcoholic beverages may ultimately determine the
sort of people who patronize a country store. A proprietor in Columbia
Falls, Maine once told me: "Most of my customers are from about age
fourteen to thirty-five — mainly fishermen, clammers and wormers. They
start coming in the store a couple hours before going out (on the mudflats)
and get drunk on beer, and come in again after the tide to buy more beer.
I sell a thousand dollars worth of beer a day!"

In South Carolina, I've noticed that a good deal of drinking goes on
round back of some country store buildings. It is hot in South Carolina
much of the year; patrons are apt to enter country stores shortly after they
open to buy that first beer of the day. Curiously — and this may be due
in part to the conservatism of the region — they will buy just one can of
beer at a time — wrapped, of course, in a small brown paper "sack" — go
round back to drink it, then return for a second, a third, and so on.
Certainly, it is cheaper to purchase it by the six-pack. But how does one
keep it cold? And wouldn't that imply drinking to excess? Proprietors
don't seem to mind selling a can at a time either. Perhaps it eases their
own consciences. Maybe they view it as more responsible drinking; a can
at a time; it slows the rate of intoxication. It also fetches them a bit more
profit.

In Maine, an equally curious practice involves the paper bag to "keep
it cold." As one proprietor explained: "They'll insist I put their beer in a
paper bag, even in January, when it's ten degrees below zero outside — to
keep it cold! But it's really so none of their neighbors can see what
they've got in the bag. They don't want people to know they drink."

There are no legal Sunday beer sales in South Carolina.
Consequently, many country stores are open only six days a week. Maine
country stores, on the contrary, are busiest after twelve noon on Sunday
when beer sales become legal.

Surviving in the country store business means long hours. "You survive by selling them what they forgot to get at the supermarket," I was
told repeatedly in both states. One advantage that Maine store owners
have long had were the "Blue Laws," which forbade supermarkets from
opening on Sunday. (Supermarkets in Maine are now open Sundays.)
That, and the Sunday afternoon and evening beer sales, have ensured that

nearly all Maine country stores are open seven days a week. In South Carolina, the older proprietors usually take Sundays off; the younger, more aggressive owners often work seven days. As one store owner near the Darlington Speedway put it: "If you ain't open, you don't get it."

In Maine, the long hours are also due to the resource-based economy. When I asked one proprietor why he opened at five-thirty in the morning, he said: "There's a lot of business between five-thirty and seven. It's probably the busiest time of the day, really. People going to work — carpenters, people who go into the woods, workmen — many of them pack their lunch right here every morning, with Italian sandwiches, sweets, a drink, cigarettes — necessities for the day, and gasoline and oil, things of that sort. So basically, what you do from five-thirty until seven is get everyone off to work."

And what makes these country store owners willing to work fifteen or sixteen hours a day, seven days a week? Is it for the money? After all, country stores do charge a bit more than supermarkets. "If you survive, that's it," a disgruntled store owner in one small South Carolina community told me. "Taxes eat me up. You can't make any money. As long as I can eat and watch television, I don't give a damn. I haven't had a vacation in eight years. The old lady (wife) won't let me have any time off."

In another small Carolina country store, the owner, a woman, said: "I like it because I can sit up here and talk all day. I never get fussed at for being late." It was the noon hour, and local men - farmers in overalls, roofers, carpenters, and mechanics — sat on worn wooden benches, eating liver mush sandwiches, pork and beans out of cans, and generous wedges of old-fashioned store cheese.

In both states, proprietors repeatedly said they liked their independence, being their own boss. Most also said they enjoyed being with people, especially listening to them tell stories.

One Carolina owner said: "There's been more deer killed and fish caught in this store than anywhere. I don't think I'd be happy doing anything else." And when I asked a proprietor in the tiny community of Centenary, South Carolina if he encouraged people to linger and socialize, he said: "Yes, I do, because after they sit there a while they buy something." A few minutes later, when I went over to the "drink box" and pulled out a bottle of soda, he said: "See what I mean?"

Indeed, Mr. Wilson, owner of Wilson's Grocery in Friendship, South Carolina, "set" me down, bought me some cheese and crackers and a bottle of "Coke Cola," and showed me the otter he had frozen in his drink box. I was much impressed, not only by his Southern hospitality and his frosty flat otter, but because Mr. Wilson, age seventy-six, still did his calculations with a pencil on a scrap of paper he had on top of his two-hundred-year-old counter. This was the real thing: An old man in an old store, with wooden benches, counters, and shelves salvaged from an even older store!

Like other old surviving country stores in both South Carolina and Maine, Wilson's Grocery is one long rectangular room with the gable end of the roof facing the road. It has a porch overhang with two gas pumps underneath. The oldest stores in both states are built of wood and in the gable-front design. In the 1940s and 1950s cement block store buildings came into vogue in South Carolina, while wood persisted in Maine. In recent years, metal buildings — perhaps more functional, but with much less charm — have been replacing wood and cinder block in both states.

Mr. Wilson and his wife live adjacent to their store in a pretty, yellow frame cottage with a tin roof. They had a large vegetable garden out back and two old black dogs dozed in the May sunshine. Mr. Wilson told me that all of his children and grandchildren were coming home for Mother's Day. There would be about twenty people all together for dinner, and his wife would do all the cooking. He wondered if I had any children of my own and seemed a little disappointed when I admitted I didn't have any. He said they made the home complete.

Wilson's Grocery does not sell beer or wine, but like all genuine Carolina country stores, they do sell cane fishing poles and crickets. But as I drove those flat roads of the Pee Dee region and began to see the differences and similarities between country stores in South Carolina and Maine, one thing continued to puzzle me. None of those cricket bins out front of country stores ever seemed to have lids. Why didn't the crickets simply escape? Finally, towards the end of May, as I was wrapping up my research and getting ready to leave for Maine, I stopped at one last country store and asked my stupid question. The owner pointed to a shiny strip of aluminum flashing perhaps six inches wide and said: "You see, that there flashin' is so smooth them crickets just slides right back down there when they tries to get out."

"Amazing!"

1990

PROFESSORS AS SCAVENGERS

"How old is that wool cap you're wearing, Allan?" my friend, Rusty, asks as we run laps around the park.

"I bought it at Charlie's Army Surplus store in Magnolia, Arkansas in 1972," I reply. The cap has a big hole in it, and there are flecks of white paint on it from when I painted a barn in Stanhope, New Jersey in 1974.

"Look, if you think this cap is old, I've got a corduroy sports jacket that I bought to wear on my first date with Linda (my wife) in 1969. She won't let me throw it out. Actually, there's still some good in it and it feels right."

A lot of my belongings are old and nearly worn out. For example, I drive a 1971 Volvo with a cracked windshield, seats all torn up, windows with black electrical tape around them to keep out the rainwater, and 156,000 miles on the odometer. The car used to be blue; it's faded to gray.

Occasionally, during our evening runs, the conversation revolves around who among our little running group is the cheapest. Most everyone agrees it's me.

"Allan doesn't even have cable TV," Rusty says. "Heck, he just got color," Kenny adds. Rusty works for the highway department; Kenny works at the paper mill. They assume that because I'm a college professor I make oodles of money. That seems to be the perception people have of life in higher education. The reality is that, except for those folks teaching at "flag-ship" and Ivy League universities, most college professors make less money than public school teachers, most of whom do not have advanced degrees. At least they have a salary scale — we don't.

I don't think I'm a skinflint, but you won't find many people more frugal than your average geography professor. We're always among the lowest paid faculty. The only ones worse off than us are the English professors. They're a starving lot. Demoralized, too. How would you like to read freshman compositions all day long for the rest of your working life?

It takes about 10 years or more to earn the B.S., M.A., and Ph.D. degrees necessary to be considered for tenure. And at age 35, when I had finished my doctorate and had nearly 10 years of teaching experience, my salary was twenty thousand. That was five years ago.

My department chairman finished his Ph.D. more than 20 years ago. He typically appears on campus wearing his favorite blue sweater with holes worn through both elbows, khaki shorts, baseball cap, cigar, and sunglasses. "Hey, they don't pay us enough around here to dress any better," he says.

What kind of society is it that pays professional athletes millions of dollars, and factory workers and truck drivers more than full professors? We're said to have the finest graduate schools in the world right here in the United States, yet many high school and some college graduates can scarcely read and write a simple sentence. Such a waste! Turn out top-notch professors full of energy, enthusiasm, and idealism; pay them as little as possible to teach poorly motivated and unprepared students; then allow them to become more disillusioned with each passing semester. Some professors drink themselves into early retirement; many concentrate less on teaching and more on research; running and writing keep me sane.

When I was teaching in North Dakota, I had a colleague who bought all of his clothing at the "Nearly New Store." Some of his suits were so baggy the crotch was down near his knees. He had a strange walk, too, a gait actually. He'd lope along with his head down and his shoulders hunched over and I never knew if it was the weight of the world or the weight of those oversized suits that was dragging him down.

I had a colleague at Livingstone College in North Carolina several years ago who didn't own a suit. "I was going to buy a suit in 1959," he explained, "but I didn't like the style." More than likely he was in graduate school back then. Graduate students, especially those in long-term programs leading to the Ph.D., are among the poorest people in the United States. Most of us in higher education have precious memories of graduate school when we lived from hand to mouth on teaching assistantships, a form of welfare that's not nearly so lucrative as real welfare!

We used to have potluck suppers in graduate school. These were always popular — no one went away hungry. I remember one potluck in particular — we sat around afterwards watching a fellow graduate student named Jeff continue to eat and eat and eat! Jeff was a skeleton. He was really starving. He wore thick glasses that were held together by adhesive tape. He wore the same old clothes everyday. I think he must have just stood his pants up at night. You couldn't get too close to Jeff, either. You didn't want to. "The old lady that runs the boarding house is pretty stingy with the heat...and the water," he explained.

I remember driving Jeff home after that potluck dinner. (This was in 1976 and I was driving my old Volvo, a 1966 model. See, I actually had a relatively newer car then. I've gotten poorer.) It was a cold, rainy night, and I stopped the Volvo in front of Jeff's rooming house. He got out carefully, as he was trying to juggle an armful of leftovers. Oops! He slipped on the wet pavement and a piece of lemon meringue pie suddenly slid off the paper plate on to the wet pavement. Jeff knelt down on the pavement; his thick glasses slipped forward as he craned his neck and said excitedly, "It's okay! It's okay! It's still good! I'll just clean it off a little." And he did! He scraped off the road dirt and carefully nudged that piece of lemon meringue pie back on to the paper plate and carefully shuffled out of the rain and ran up to his room.

Jeff eventually dropped out of graduate school. Unlike me, he never became a college professor. Last I heard, he was living in Philadelphia where he'd enrolled in a course in culinary arts. I don't suppose he'll be cooking gourmet dinners for many college professors.

1991

PACKING FOR MAINE

Ricky and I were on a Friday afternoon run. We ran westward out of town on an old railroad bed adjacent to the highway. The tracks had been pulled up years ago, and now it was just gravel with some clumps of grass and weeds sprouting here and there. Even though the weather was unseasonably cool, we were on the lookout for snakes — copperheads and rattlers especially — as several dead ones were flattened on the highway. And when the weeds eventually got too thick for us to see where we were planting our feet, we jumped the ditch — this time of year full of blue flag iris and honeysuckle — and got up on the tar road.

I asked Ricky if he was packed yet.

"Oh, yeah. But I can't decide whether to bring my video camera. They take your picture when you get on the boat and lots of times during the cruise itself, and I'm bringing my 35mm camera anyway...But...we're gonna go past that island where they filmed Gilligan's Island, and they say it's just beautiful!"

Ricky and his wife were going on a Caribbean cruise to celebrate their 25th wedding anniversary. He told me about some of the things it offered: No less than eight meals a day, from breakfast in bed to a 1:30 a.m. buffet; a jogging track, sauna, and gym with exercise machines; a swimming pool, or pools, I can't recall how many; aerobics, and all sorts of indoor and outdoor sports activities; at least two live shows every night; stops at Nassau and Freeport in the Bahamas; and, of course, casino gambling. The whole thing sounded absolutely dreadful to me — so phony, everything pre-planned and pre-arranged, with every need and whim satisfied.

But I didn't tell Ricky my thoughts. I just said, "Wow! That's something!" Aside from running, Ricky and I have little else in common. Maybe that's why we enjoy each other's company. He broadens my horizons, and in a very small way, perhaps I broaden his. He can't understand, for example, my fascination with backwater places down in Mexico. His perception of Mexico is derived from movies and television, while mine comes from having spent time there. He always cautions me, "Boy, you better watch yourself down there!" I would tell him about the salads and dairy products I didn't dare eat and the water I didn't dare drink, the seedy hotels I sometimes stayed in. Ricky delighted in hearing about all the hardships of Mexican travel. I guess it reinforced what he already believed about the place.

We ran on, and I thought of my research trips to the mountains of

Michoacán, Mexico: No advance reservations, no itinerary; I simply bought a ticket on a night flight to Mexico City and went. From there, I rode second-class buses and trains, tried to speak Spanish with the locals, and saw the real Mexico that tourists never see. I would run the whole gamut of emotions and experiences — boredom, excitement, the antici-pation of a new place, the perception of danger, a little bit of fear, fatigue, depression, delight, hunger, some pain, sickness, sorrow, and much joy. Sometimes I came home exhausted — gaunt, wasted away, my clothes draped over my skeletal body. But I usually felt that the journey had changed my life, had made me more human, had made me a kinder, more sympathetic person. "And you want to go back there?" Ricky would shake his head in disbelief. He even suggested I join him on the cruise. "We can run on the boat, past all those women in their bikinis," Ricky joked. "You don't need to go to Mexico. You can do all the research you want, right there on that boat!"

We ran into a northwest breeze. Ricky told me about all the clothes he had packed, and presumably, would need for the various activities and social engagements during the cruise. I thought of the single piece of "carry-on" luggage I always took to Mexico.

Last spring, Ricky told me about his vacation to Orlando, Florida, to Disneyworld, another destination that's clean and safe and fake. Don't Americans want to see anything real anymore? It got me to thinking: If people lose contact with real places — natural as opposed to artificial landscapes, populated with real indigenous cultures who understand those places — why should they care when real places are destroyed? In other words, if they're satisfied to go to Disneyworld, or to see the Bahamas from a luxury cruise liner, why should they care if the farms and fields and woods in their own neighborhoods are vanishing? Why should they care when the natural world is transformed into a shopping mall, subdivision, or toxic waste dump? They can always indulge themselves in a "Carnival Fun Cruise."

Ricky had a dark, even tan for so early in May. He and his wife had been making regular visits to the tanning salon to "get ready for the cruise." Ricky looked much younger than his 43 years. We picked up the pace, and I began to wonder if he ran for one of the main reasons that I run — to see the wild flowers in the spring, the bare trees in winter, and the snakes and other creatures in their natural habitats. I also wondered why, as a society, we've become so preoccupied with our appearance, so obsessed with looking young. I was fixating on the blue flag iris bloom-ing in the ditch. I mentioned the flowers to Ricky, but he didn't seem to pay much attention. I thought of the blue flag that would be coming up by the stream that drains the heath behind our camp in Gouldsboro, in a month or so.

It wouldn't be long, and my wife, Linda, and I, and our old dog, Hallie, would be driving down the dirt road — through blueberry fields, then the pines and aspens and poplars, and finally, the alders and tamaraks, before crossing over the stream — where the blue flag would soon be coming out — and up the slight incline to our camp on Jones Pond. Oh, I guess it's a vacation, in that we've both finished the school year and aren't teaching classes; but we like to think of it as our other life. For me, it has always been the best life.

It's no Carnival Cruise. It's a real place, full of black flies, deer flies, mosquitoes, and horse flies. There's no electricity, telephone or running water. There's a wood stove, a small Coleman cooking stove, an ice chest, kerosene lamps, and a battery operated radio. That's plenty. Then there's the pond, the calling of the loons, the sounding of the Bluenose Ferry — in the morning when it leaves Bar Harbor and again at night when it returns — and of course, there's our own conversation, the books and magazines we're reading, the words I write.

Hallie may rediscover her old shoe, an old bone, or a stick she wants us to toss. Or, maybe she'll chase a squirrel or a rabbit or tree a porcupine. The pond will be freezing cold when we arrive in early June, but we'll swim in it anyway. We have no choice — there's no shower or bathtub. The outhouse will have lots of spiders and ants, and maybe some mice and a garter snake or two. We'll caulk and paint the old rowboat and haul it down to the water. We'll cut and stack the firewood, which we'll need as long as the frogs continue peeping in the cool evenings. We'll clear away the new saplings and reclaim the camp from the encroaching woods. We'll renew old friendships and acquaintances, and hear about the winter and the economy and the Downeast world of real people and real places.

Ricky and I didn't see any live snakes on our run that afternoon. He went home to finish packing for his Caribbean cruise. I started packing for Maine.

1992

AT CAMP ON JONES POND

We arrived at Jones Pond on June 2, my birthday. We broke down twice on the drive up from South Carolina. The engine started missing less than an hour into the trip!

It was a cracked sparkplug — of all things! I fixed it myself. The second day out, we broke down just over the New Jersey border — of all places! It was raining buckets. We had to get towed. The ground wire had broken off the alternator.

And then we got stopped by the New Jersey State Police.

"Where are you going?" the officer asks.

"Maine."

"Do you realize the speed limit is 50 miles per hour right here?"

"Uh."

"I clocked you at nearly 65!"

"Sixty-five! No way. I might have been doing 55, but 65? I'm shocked!"

"I don't want to banter with you, sir. I got you on the radar gun."

He gave me a warning. We reached camp that evening. Oh, thank you, Lord!

I've been waiting for this day since last August.

It's raining again. There is no electricity here — no television, lights or phone — nothing. Nor is there running water. We rely on the pond for bathing, a neighbor's well for drinking water, kerosene lamps for light, a wood stove for heat, and an outhouse built in 1978 with boards scavenged from a friend's fallen barn. One board measures 18 inches in width and has a knothole for peering out.

"An outhouse!" a colleague once shrieked, when I told her how my wife, Linda, and I spend our summers. She walked off muttering something about each to his own before I could tell her how proud I am of that privy. It's such an improvement after my original wilderness outhouse — a hole in the ground surrounded by a lean-to of fir boughs. A balsam tree had stood in front for cover.

It she had only known what it was like my first summer in this camp, in 1973. I was 22 then, and still in college. I kept a journal that summer and wrote mostly about the rain, fog, mosquitoes, discomfort, and loneliness. I suppose it was typical of a self-centered college student; to insulate oneself from the rest of the world; to think only of one's own misery.

I remember coming home evenings from a landscaping job in

Harrington that summer, building a camp fire on the rocks below, and cooking hotdogs among the mosquitoes. Occasionally, I caught bass, drove sharp sticks through them, and roasted the fish over the flames. The fishing isn't what it used to be. I worried that the planet might be dying back then. I still do. But at least now I have the memories of when the fishing was better.

The camp was tiny then; just 10 feet by 12. It had a rough floor of random-width pine planks that had dried out over the years. There were cracks as wide as three quarters of an inch which invited hordes of mosquitoes. I had an old iron bed and springs, but no real mattress. I slept fitfully on a two-inch-thick piece of foam rubber which molded itself around the curves of my body as it swayed over the coiled springs. Later, I tried placing a four-by-eight foot sheet of plywood on the springs with the foam rubber mattress atop it, but the bed rocked and rolled like a small boat in deep swells. An old picnic table but no chairs, a pine trunk for storing canned food, the makeshift bed, a tiny wall mirror, and a kerosene barn lantern with a red globe that gave off very little light, were my only furnishings. There were no screens on the three windows, which were nailed shut. The front door stood almost three feet above the sloping ledge on which the structure rests, and I had to climb up on a big granite boulder and hurl myself inside.

A child's idea of paradise; I had built the 10-by-12 foot camp in 1966, when I was 15 years old. My father was with me when I strung out the original chalkline. He had suggested I build it among the ruins of an old stone wall that runs along the bank, just up from the water's edge. To my father, the camp would have been a teenaged boy's hut or hiding place in the woods. I don't think he ever imagined it as my future home. But to me, it was to be something more substantial; I imagined myself living here permanently some day, so I built the camp on a ledge, a good 75 feet back from the pond.

To buy a piece of land in Maine, and to build on it my very own camp, had been my obsession since I was about 12. My parents encouraged me; they loaned me the money, which I slowly repaid by mowing lawns. And in 1965, when I was only 14, I bought this half acre for less than $500.

We strung the original chalkline while on vacation in Maine in July of 1966. Then my father retreated to his fishing pole, while I began digging the post holes. And during the next two weeks, I was able to set down the cedar posts, sills, joists, and floor of random-width planks.

My father and I went fishing the last night of our vacation. "Take one more cast," he had said, again and again that evening, as the sky changed from blue to orange to black. "Maybe we'll see some animals tonight," he said, as we drove out the dirt road in darkness. We stopped for an ice cream cone on our way back to our summer home in Steuben, and that night he died. My father had a massive heart attack. He was only 48.

My mother and I moved to Maine from New Jersey later that summer. We sold our house there, and moved to our old Cape Cod house in Steuben. And on weekends in the fall, until the snow fell, I worked on the camp. It was the only autumn I've ever spent at Jones Pond, and I remember sitting on the ridge pole, marveling at the brilliant colors. It wasn't a bad place to be alone, and on many a fall afternoon in present-day South Carolina, I've sat at my desk and fantasized about flying home to Jones Pond. I got the walls and roof boarded and tar papered that fall, and that's essentially how the camp remained until Linda and I were married.

When we arrived in the summer of 1976, Linda insisted on some improvements. We covered the floor with linoleum, replaced the Granite boulder with wooden steps, put screens on the windows, and tried to make the camp mosquito-proof, but it was still "wicked hard living." There was still no heat — you can freeze to death here in June — and the 10 by 12 foot hovel tested our relationship.

We never have solved the mosquito problem, probably because we are surrounded on three sides by water. A wooded, bullfrog heath lies to the north, Fred's Cove to the east, then Bar Point, and finally the main body of the pond to the south. In the west, the pond empties into Frenchman Bay, and in the morning and again at night, we can hear the departure and return of the Bluenose, the ferry to and from Nova Scotia.

In the late 1970s, we popped open a portion of the roof and built a four by eight foot sleeping loft. It had a window in front resembling a sort of funny looking dormer, but it leaked like a sieve when it rained, and we were always hitting our heads on the two by fours. Still needing space, we added a tiny sun porch in the early 1980s, but I installed the corrugated fiberglass roofing incorrectly and it flapped and fluttered when the wind blew, and it too leaked in the rain. And worse, the rounded hollows where the roofing adjoined the main roof made an ideal habitat for bats that seemed to thrive and multiply with each passing summer.

This camp and lifestyle represent the fulfillment — and persistence — of a childhood dream. As a youth, I studied the maps on my bedroom walls, dreamed of trekking to distant backwaters and holing up in a cabin in the wilderness. My life became the dream. I eventually became a geography professor, yet squirreled away as much time as possible each summer for living at the camp.

But our standard of living has been hand to mouth. I was in graduate school on and off — between teaching jobs — until the mid-1980s, and we muddled along in academic poverty. One summer, when we had gotten down to less than $40, we gathered up all of our nonessentials and sold them at the Even Exchange — a local second-hand shop. If we could hang on until blueberry season we could earn enough money raking to get back to the classroom, which, unfortunately, has always been more than a thousand miles from here. Still, the dream has persisted despite the bewilderment of friends and family.

In 1985, with a teaching job at a state college in North Dakota, but my doctoral dissertation still unfinished, we built a 16-by-16-foot addition with a wood stove and double hung windows with screens and a real loft with skylights. Such luxury! I finished my dissertation that year, and we dreamed of further improvements.

The new camp opened into the old, which we had left intact for sentimental reasons. But the cedar posts on which it rested had rotted over the years, as had the sills, and some of the floorboards. The building dipped down on one end; and, of course, we still had the sun porch with the leaky corrugated roof and the bats in residence. And because of the many cracks and crevices, and doors and windows that didn't fit properly, the camp was still infested with black flies and mosquitoes — so bad were they that we slept under a net.

We tried to think of ways we might remodel and save the old camp. So many precious memories were housed in that 10-by-12-foot shack; we just couldn't bring ourselves to tear it down. But there was no practical solution to the ravages of time or to the limitations of a tiny structure built by a 15-year-old boy with marginal carpentry skills.

Finally, in 1989, we pulled the old camp down. And what a task! Teenaged boys, I learned, love to drive nails. Some of those eight-inch-wide sheathing boards had five or six nails per stud. There were spikes and carriage bolts in every corner post and rafter plate. It was not built to be torn down — ever! It was all done according to the 1920 edition of the *Audel's Carpenters and Builders Guide* that my father had picked up at a used book shop in Newark, New Jersey, and that I carried around with me by freshman year of high school.

In place of the old 10-by-12 foot camp we added another room, 14-by-16 feet, which made the entire structure now measure 16-by-30 feet. The window at the end of the new second-story loft looks out over Fred's Cove, and it is from here that I write. I'm sitting on that same pine trunk that I used my first summer here in 1973; my feet are resting on those same random-width floorboards. We salvaged them; decided they were just right for the floor of the loft.

1992

5

OLD DOGS AND MARATHON RUNNERS

At 12 and a half years of age, my dog, Hallie, isn't quite the runner she used to be. She's still pretty fast on the take-off, but unlike the old days when she ran round and round in tight circles and never seemed to tire, nowadays it only takes 10 or 15 minutes of stick fetching before she slumps in the grass and pants. I wonder if Hallie realizes she's gotten old and doesn't have too many years left to run? While she's just as sweet and lovable as ever, my wife, Linda, and I have noticed she sleeps a lot more now too. She's also gained some weight, and her eyes are getting cataracts; they're not as bright and clear as they once were.

Hallie was born to run. She's a collie/setter mix; black and white, with a long satiny coat. She looks a lot like a Border Collie, except a little taller, with soft ears that flop down rather than stand up.

Along with Linda, Hallie is the love of my life. She sleeps at my bedside at night, and I don't mind it a bit that I sometimes wake up with tufts of Hallie's fur clinging to my beard. Nor do I mind the occasional wet dog muzzle in my face at three or four o'clock on a winter morning. I usually need to make a nightly trip to the bathroom myself; like Hallie, I'm getting older too.

Watching Hallie grow from puppyhood to old age these past 12 years has helped me to accept the inevitable — that we're all going to slow down; that none of us are getting out of this alive.

Like Hallie, running has always been, and continues to be, one of my passions. I've been a long distance runner since age 15, and a marathoner since my senior year at Sumner High School in East Sullivan in 1969. I ran my first marathon at Boston that April, and on April 3 of this year, I ran my 42nd, at a place called Ellerbe Springs in the piedmont of North Carolina. I live in Marion, South Carolina, down on the coastal plain, where it's completely flat. Ellerbe is about 70 miles north of here. It's just above the fall-line, about 12 miles north of Rockingham, where they race stock cars. Ellerbe Springs lies in an undulating area of sedimentary rocks just south of the Uwharrie Mountains.

"They say it's the mother of all marathons," a friend commented, when I mentioned the upcoming Ellerbe Springs race. Indeed, the entry blank had stated: "This is a very hilly and demanding course." The course record was also listed: 3:03:58 (three hours, three minutes, and 58 seconds). By comparison, the course record for the Charlotte Marathon, another hilly race — much tougher than Boston — is 2:16.

What was I getting into? I thought about backing out. After all, I've run Boston five times, the Mardi Gras Marathon, the Mile High in Denver, the New York City Marathon, to name a few. After 41 of these insane races, what was there to prove?

But then my friend, Roger, who is 31, and trying to rebuild his life after a painful divorce, said he was "definitely going to give Ellerbe Springs a try." I said, "Well, if you're going, then I might as well try it too." I thought: Like old Hallie, there's going to come a day when I can no longer do this sort of thing, so I might as well keep running marathons as long as I'm able.

I'd had a good winter, too. In December, for some unexplained reason, I ran 100 miles one week. In all these years of running, I'd never had a 100-mile week. And it didn't kill me. I thought, I ought to do this more often!

I went to Mexico after Christmas, where I trained at nearly 8,000 feet. Every morning at about eight o'clock, I'd arrive at the plaza in Pátzcuaro, an old colonial town deep in the mountains of Michoacán State. I'd then run breathless laps around the plaza for the next hour and a half, as though I just couldn't stop. Some of the locals began calling me "El Corriador" — the runner. But I was having fun observing another culture, watching this old Mexican town come to life.

Two weeks after returning from Mexico, I ran the Charlotte Marathon in 3:07:05, which was half a minute faster than my best time in 1973, when I was 21 years old. I ran a wind-aided 2:44:12 for a personal best in the 1975 Boston Marathon, but from that race on, it's been all downhill. I haven't run a sub-three-hour race since 1982. My best time last year was 3:11, so the 3:07 race at Charlotte really surprised and delighted me.

Maybe at age 41 I had learned something about runners — that as we get older, we simply need to run more, not less! We might not be able to run as fast as we used to, but maybe if we train harder and longer, we can still run almost as fast. Speed leaves us at an early age, but endurance...well, it endures, and for many years longer than we realize. For most of our existence on this earth, we humans have been nomadic hunter-gatherers, not sedentary farmers. Our bodies are built to cover long distances. All we have to do is use them.

I returned to Mexico in March, where I've been working on a research project in cultural geography (my profession). I ran in the mornings again, then spent my afternoons hiking — around cities, towns, and Indian villages; across the countryside; even to the top of a volcano. When I returned from Mexico I was five pounds lighter. At 145 pounds, I weighed less than when I ran high school cross-country.

Linda and I had been observing the Lenten fast, so on Friday, April 2, she prepared a meatless meal of baked potatoes, macaroni and cheese, beans, carrots, and croissants. Later that evening, I snacked on some taco chips and salsa — more carbohydrate packing.

I chased down two English muffins and jelly with a Coke Classic in the morning, then drove up to Ellerbe Springs, North Carolina. I guess I was pretty nervous, because I recall plucking a few tufts of Hallie's fur out of my beard as I drove. Bless her heart. (Linda and I have often joked about how much money someone could offer us for that old dog. "Why if someone were to offer us a million dollars for Hallie, and she only had a few days to live, we'd still turn it down!" That sort of talk. Hallie cost us $20. Isn't it wonderful that the best things in life are seldom the most expensive!)

Roger and I agreed we were going to run the first five miles conservatively...and we did. It was a clear, crisp, and breezy morning, and the hills were all that we had been warned they were. Roger made a pit stop at three miles, and I moved ahead. I got the "urge" around five miles, and he pulled ahead. I didn't catch Roger until mile 11, when I put on a mid-race surge.

The hills only seemed to get longer and steeper, the sun, hotter. I felt my lily-white skin begin to fry. My eyes began stinging from salty sweat. It was suddenly much warmer now; water rained from my head and down my face and I used my hands as a windshield wiper. Whereas earlier I had worried about having to make a pit stop, now I worried about dehydration. It was three miles between every cup of water, and the hills continued to come at us. The downhills were especially steep and jarring. You had to keep braking, or else you'd go tumbling. The road twisted and turned so much that you always felt one leg being yanked and stretched to the point of dismemberment, while the other was being pushed up through your hip socket. Runners began dropping back to us, however, as the miles wore on. They were wasted, corpse-like creatures — apparitions almost — that somehow defied gravity and kept creeping forward, perhaps because they knew there was no other way, save total humiliation, failure, and defeat. My heart went out to them...but only for a minute; I still had a long way to go. But Roger and I had done our training and were ready for whatever came at us; or so I thought.

I turned onto the main highway at mile 25, when a pickup truck towing a long horse trailer rolled across my path. I hit the brakes, then felt a sharp pain in my ribs — a muscle spasm. I got started again, and had run 100 yards or so down the highway, when a gray-haired "high society-type" woman pulled out of a long driveway in a shiny new Lincoln Town Car and into my path. And then I nearly got blown off the road by a couple of tractor-trailers. Was this ordeal ever going to end?

The finish was down a steep hill. It was dirt and loose gravel, and I came barreling across the line, stumbled, and fell into a mud puddle. I tried to get up, but my right leg cramped and I toppled into a thornbush and scratched up my knee. It took three handlers to finally haul me out of the thicket and the mud and get me back on my feet. A woman grabbed my arm and started taking my pulse. I said, "I don't think I'm quite dead yet."

There were only 82 finishers. A new course record was set at 2:52. Only two runners broke three hours. I finished 11th in 3:16; Roger was 13th in 3:18; the second place finisher was 47 years old!

Roger and I agreed we'd never run this race again, but I sort of think we will. Marathons have a way of calling you back. (I've run the Charlotte Marathon nine times. It's held in early January when the weather there is typically cool — 40's — and raining.) So who knows? If that 47-year-old can break three hours on this course, maybe we can too. Dream on!

When I got home that evening — all gimped up, sunburned, looking like a boiled Maine lobster — I collapsed on the sofa and tried to take a nap. But it was no use — I was too exhausted to fall asleep, my legs were still throbbing.

So I went outside and threw a stick for Hallie. She'd charge after it, pick it up, drop it, then bark for me to come get it. And I did. Like a well-trained dog, I dutifully padded across the yard, retrieved Hallie's stick, and tossed it several more times. She tired after about 15 minutes, plopped to the grass, lifted and flicked her magnificent feathered tail, opened her long muzzle and rolled out her pink tongue and panted contentedly. No, Hallie's not the runner she used to be; but then, neither am I.

1993

6

THE EDUCATION OF A GEOGRAPHER

In the history of life the less specialized forms have tended to survive and flourish, whereas the functionally self-limiting types have become fossils.

The above quotation is from the late Carl Sauer, distinguished professor of cultural geography at the University of California at Berkeley. Sauer argues that in this age of ever-increasing specialization, where scholars seem to be learning more and more about less and less, geographers are by nature generalists who try to understand the earth as the home of humans. This essay is about the process of becoming a geographer, a vocation that most Americans are only vaguely aware exists. While there are hundreds of thousands of counselors, dentists, doctors, engineers, journalists, lawyers, psychologists, sociologists and teachers, the Association of American Geographers, the largest professional organization of geographers in the United States, has slightly more than 6,000 members.

Hardly anyone in my graduating class at Sumner High School in 1969 went to college out-of-state. Most went to one of the branches of the University of Maine; I went to college in southern Arkansas...on a 350cc Yamaha motorcycle. "Arkansas? Why are you going there?" my friends had asked me. I wasn't really sure. The tuition was much lower there. And I wanted to play college baseball and they had a longer season in Arkansas.

I also planned to run cross-country and major in fine arts, but I suspect there were other, perhaps more cerebral and even more compelling reasons for going to college so far from home. I had a curiosity about places, and I had never been south of Pennsylvania or west of Illinois.

When I was a child, maps had always adorned my bedroom walls. I studied them constantly, wondering what those places were like. But I was happiest when exploring the woods or roaming the countryside. I craved freedom. I disdained conformity. I didn't want to fit in. My heroes were always the loners who left the girl behind and headed off into the wilderness. So I knew I wanted to travel, but not in the military way, where you live in the artificial society of the base with a set of rules and regulations, insulated from local culture.

I have since learned that geographers are likely to be the types of people who embrace other cultures, rather than suppressing or supplanting them. Real geographers try to live as close to indigenous cultures and their landscapes as possible. Writing more than 40 years ago, Carl Sauer suggested that "geographers should be content to camp out at the end of the day." That may not always be possible in the 20th century, in a world where geography is becoming increasingly urban. Contemporary geographers are more likely to buy a plane ticket to some Third World backwater, hole up in a seedy hotel and then get sick as a dog trying to digest the local food.

Real geographers are likely to be unassailable. They want as few rules as possible. They want to find their own answers to problems at their own pace. They don't want the advice of tour guides or travel agents. It takes a long time to become a geographer. It also takes some courage. Not the sort of courage needed to defend, conquer and defeat; rather, the courage to move among strangers in unfamiliar societies; the courage to trust other cultures rather than eye them with contempt because they are different from us. Real geographers possess the kind of courage that allows you to wander in to the sorts of places where you just shrug your shoulders and say, "Oh well, when God wants me I guess he'll come and get me!"

What I had no way of knowing when I took off on that motorcycle in 1969 was that I inherently possessed many of those qualities needed to make a geographer. But I didn't even know such a field existed. Like most people, I assumed that geography was little more than memorizing the locations of places on a map.

There is much more to geography than places-names on a map. While it is true that geography is the science of location, and that maps are the principal tools of geographers, simple map location without description supported by explanation is hardly geography. And those who think they know something of geography simply by memorizing the locations of cities, countries and rivers know almost nothing. While others who fear they know little about geography may actually know far more about the character of their own local geography than professional geographers. For example, I am sure there are many people on Beals Island who know far more about the local families, history, property values, fauna and flora, tides and weather, than I. Geography is a humbling profession. You soon realize that no matter how much you think you know about the world, you really know nothing at all. And it's constantly changing; nothing stays the same for long. So you go to Beals, you spend time there, and you try to learn all you can from the experts who have lived and prospered there. Those residents are the true geographers, and for a while you must become their student until you eventually begin to understand the character of the place.

Geography is not a trivial pursuit. If you want to know the average annual rainfall, the capital city, the per capita income, the population, the highest mountain, or longest river, you can look it up. That's what atlases are for. But that's not really doing geography; it's more like playing Jeopardy. Those facts won't tell you what it's really like to live there, any more than two weeks or two months or two years spent at Club Med in Cancun, Mexico, will tell you about the geography of the Yucatan Peninsula. Such factual information won't necessarily help you solve important problems either, like, why are the Brazilians destroying their rain forest? What solutions can be found? One has to dig much deeper and find creative ways to solve problems, and that's what geographers do.

There is a geography of nearly everything: AIDS cases in Maine; the murder rate in Maine's cities; child hunger in Maine's counties; the origins of NBA players; the distribution of stock car races and race fans in the United States; the frequency of tornadoes in the Middle West. These are just some examples of topics that are geographical. Virtually anything that can be placed on a map is in the realm of geography. So, we are generalists who employ a variety of methods to solve problems. The Association of American Geographers lists 35 specialty groups, ranging from agriculture, climatology, economics, and ecology to medical geography, population, politics, Marxist geography, and women's studies. (About 10 percent of all AAG members are women. Despite their small numbers, women geographers have historically been important in nearly all of geography's subfields.) Whereas some geographers specialize in one subfield, such as Third World urbanization, or one region, such as Subsaharan Africa, others delve into a variety of regions and subfields. In my own case, I teach courses in both human and physical geography, as well as regional courses on Africa, Europe, Latin America, North America, and the Middle East.

Like myself, most geographers do not start out intending to major in geography. Most incoming college freshmen have no idea there's such a thing as a geography major. They've probably never met anyone who held the title of geographer. Even Indiana Jones claimed to be an anthropologist, archeologist, or something of the sort. And unlike psychologists, geographers never get to appear on *Donohue* or the *Oprah Winfrey Show*, although *Good Morning America* does occasionally have a geography segment with Harm de Blij, a professor at the University of Miami.

Unfortunately, geography is a neglected subject at all levels in the United States. Why? Perhaps because we're so rich in land and resources we haven't needed geography as much as, say, the United Kingdom, a tiny island nation-state in Western Europe that once had an empire that covered 27 percent of the earth's surface. The British had colonies all over the globe; it is not surprising that geography is the third-most popular academic major at British universities. By contrast, the United States is still somewhat of an isolationist nation. Most of the world knows far more about us than we do about them.

Only about 50 percent of the colleges in the United States offer courses in geography. Here in Maine, only the University of Maine at Farmington and the University of Southern Maine offer majors. The University of Maine has a center for geographic information but no geography major. The other branches of the university system offer little or nothing. Maine ranks near the bottom of the 50 states in geographic education at the college level. Thank heavens I went to college in Arkansas!

There was only one geographer at Southern Arkansas University when I arrived there in 1969, and thanks to him, I became aware of geography's importance. His name was Huddlestun. He was short, bald, bespectacled and nearing retirement. And on weekends, he could be seen leaving his office wearing a pith helmet and sunglasses, on his way to some secret fishing hole. Professor Huddleston was my mentor. He'd stroll in, crack a joke or two, then pepper his lecture with wonderful stories about people and places I hardly knew existed. And if he hadn't seen the place himself, he'd say something like, "Now that seems like an interesting place for a geographer to visit." And I'd think, "Yeah. Yeah."

As much as I admired his knowledge, I respected him for his honesty. He once asked me, a college freshman, "Allan, how do you pronounce the names Aroostook and Orono?" He was originally from Illinois and had never visited Maine. After a few courses with Huddlestun, I realized my interest in drawing and painting landscapes went much deeper; I wanted to understand the character of those landscapes, so I changed my major from fine arts to geography.

My curiosity about places eventually led me to Western Kentucky University for a master's degree and to the University of Northern Colorado for a doctorate. And like a true geographer, I've since taught in a number of states, including Maine, Mississippi, North Carolina, North Dakota, and South Carolina, where I'm now an associate professor at Francis Marion University.

Most professional geographers are not teachers or professors, nor do most hold advanced academic degrees. Many excellent job opportunities are available to people with undergraduate degrees in geography. Some of the job titles held by people with geography backgrounds are as follows: aerial phorograph interpretators and remote sensors, cartographers, ecologists, foreign service officers, foresters, journalists, location analysts, urban and regional planners, soil scientists, real estate agents, travel agents and consultants. There are more opportunities than I have space to mention here, because geography is necessary to our economic survival. For example, the single most important reason why businesses fail is their location. It is not surprising that successful franchises like McDonald's or Red Lobster hire location analysts (geographers) to help them choose the best sites for their restaurants. And as our country and planet become more populated, geographers will be called upon to find solutions to numerous economic environmental, political, and social problems.

The ideas and opinions here are my own and don't necessarily represent the geography profession as a whole. While I consider myself a cultural geographer with a humanistic outlook, there are all sorts of geographers (physical, economic, political, etc.) who may view the field of geography in a different light. We welcome diversity. What brings geographers together is the belief that geography is important because it involves everyone and everything that can be placed on a map. As one geographer succinctly put it, "Geography is what geographers do!"

1993

7

THE MASTER CYLINDER

My friend, Randy, who recently celebrated his 45th birthday, runs 80 to 120 miles every week. He usually runs twice a day. But running is only one of Randy's passions; he also loves to smoke pot and guzzle beer. "I'm a man of many addictions," Randy freely admits. "I like to kick back and git tore up."

Randy wasn't always a runner. Back in his college days he smoked regular cigarettes besides marijuana, drank beer, and weighed more than 180 pounds. In his late 20s he took up long-distance running. His weight dropped to about 140; he gave up cigarettes, but not the marijuana and the beer. If anything, he seems to use his running as an excuse to drink even more. As his friend Lance likes to joke, "Oh, Randy's not drinking any more; he's just not drinking any less."

If I were asked to describe Randy, I'd say he was kind, compassionate, generous, intelligent, open-minded, sensitive, and conventionally religious. Like a good Southern Baptist, he puts on a coat and tie every Sunday, attends church services, and leaves a hefty sum on the plate. He also admits he likes to sit in the balcony, so he can get a better look at all the women. Randy's not married; although, even if he were, I'd think he'd want to sit in the balcony.

A large billboard near Interstate 95 in eastern South Carolina advertises "The Master Cylinder," a 24-ounce can of Schlitz "Bull" Malt Liquor. The advertising is aimed at lower-income black males. And judging from the sheer number of these cans strewn along South Carolina's roadsides, the advertising campaign has been very successful. Indeed, the word is out that the "Bull" will get you "on your way" in a hurry. Southern white males rarely drink malt liquor, simply because they know that's what poor blacks drink. In the South, where status seems to mean everything, it's important to do things right. Southern white males are more likely to drink ordinary American beers like Coors, or Budweiser, or perhaps Miller "Genuine Draft," a Carolina favorite, because the Miller people currently sponsor the NASCAR (stock car) races.

Here in the South, the Protestant work ethic has given way to the Protestant drinking ethic. I've lived in five Southern states, and it appears, to me at least, that the deeper you go into the Bible Belt, the faster the alcohol flows. Is it due to the Southern heat and humidity? I doubt it; not when nearly every Southern automobile, home, and workplace is air-conditioned. I don't think alcohol consumption has much to do with climate. I doubt it ever did; rather, I think it's mostly cultural. "Bubba," the typical Southern white, pickup-truck-driving rural male likes to "git tore up," and evidently his black contemporaries are enthusiastically following his example. There's no history in the rural South of responsible social drinking — say, a glass of wine to enhance a meal. Except for a tiny aristocracy, the average rural Southerner, or "cracker" as they once were called, has either been a teetotaler, or has gradually gone from moonshine to Budweiser and Boone's Farm.

Recently, a half dozen members of our local health and fitness club cleaned up a roadside park along the main highway just east of town. Of course, Randy, our big environmentalist, organized the cleanup. Along with his aforementioned passions, Randy is also passionate about preserving the environment. He's also counting down his remaining years at the Health Department, and dreams of hiking in the Rocky Mountains or the Sierras when he retires in about a decade. Altogether, we filled more than 30 large plastic trash bags with litter, most of it empty liquor containers; all of them dropped since we cleaned the park exactly a year ago. No returnable bottle bill in South Carolina; just mounds of beer, malt liquor, gin, rum, tequila, vodka, wine and whiskey bottles. I think that nearly every brand in North America must have been represented in that tiny park, but Canadian Club Whiskey, Boone's Farm Wine, Schlitz "Bull" Malt Liquor, Coors and Budweiser beers were among the favorites.

In places the bottles and cans were so thick we had to scoop them up with a long handled shovel — those plus some used condoms and a toilet seat! Indeed, a few hours of trash collecting will tell you a lot about the society in which you live.

I learned recently that this northeastern region of South Carolina's coastal plain leads the United States in fetal alcohol syndrome. I guess this shouldn't have surprised me, as we rank near the bottom of the U.S. in most social and economic indices; and I've watched shoppers at local supermarkets wheeling out carts filled to the brim with beer "suitcases," malt liquor, and fortified wines. Where were their groceries? This reminds me of a comment a college friend of mine made in Arkansas more than 20 years ago: "I never eat when I'm drinking." Evidently he didn't want any food slowing down his intoxication. He died several years ago.

One convenience store in a nearby community advertises cases (24 cans) of Miller "Genuine Draft" beer for $7.99. I've never seen beer sold so cheaply as in South Carolina; nor have I ever seen so many convenience stores. Our town, with some 10,000 residents, has more than a dozen, plus five supermarkets, and six Red Dot, or state-run liquor stores which sell hard liquor.

Most of my friends in the health club are either deep into alcohol or the other extreme, recovering alcoholics. One friend finally quit drinking after he nearly got his head lopped off in the turret of an army tank while on a S.C. National Guard training weekend. He said, "I used to drink a 12-pack of beer, then I'd get in that tank. I damn near got my head cut off! Hell, I used to drive my car up a tree about every other weekend. I like to killed myself drinking."

But Randy says, "On weekends, I usually get in a long run in the morning, so I can kick back and git tore up the rest of the day. I like to watch stock car racing on the big screen TV, drink a 12-pack, and smoke a little dope." Randy is a "big-time" Rusty Wallace fan. He even has a life-sized poster of the NASCAR driver in his kitchen. Indeed, Randy talks about "Rusty" as if he were an old high school buddy.

Lately, though, Randy's been, as he puts it, "getting busted" on the highway. He's been stopped by the police three times in the last month. Randy sometimes drives to the Darlington or Charlotte speedways, and he also likes to attend the home games of the University of South Carolina Gamecocks football team. "I kinda like to tailgate (party) a little before the game," Randy explains. I had never heard of tailgating before I moved to South Carolina in 1986. Apparently it's a big thing here: football fans, men mostly (who seem to me, at least, to be much too old for this nonsense), sit in the parking lot drinking liquor for several hours before the game starts. According to Randy, "We start drinking about eight or nine o'clock in the morning so that we're tore up by game-time. We sober up a little during the game so we can drive home. One of us makes sure he stays sober enough to drive so the rest of us can drink on the way home."

Southern males often refuse to grow up. And oddly, their wives and girlfriends don't seem to object. On the contrary, they just accept it as typical male, or Bubba behavior. I've seen gray-haired 50-ish looking men cruising down the interstate highway in Cadillacs and Lincolns adorned with Carolina Gamecock or Clemson University flags. Are they really that crazy about football? Absolutely. Many Southerners know their college football statistics the way I knew Major League Baseball batting averages when I was 10 years old! Others, however, use the game as a form of ritual drinking — it's just an excuse to "get tore up," especially if it's a close game and their team wins, or loses a squeaker. These perpetual adolescents might be respected members of their communities, but on football weekends, they act like 20-year-old fraternity brothers.

Why do Southern women tolerate boorish behavior by their men? I have a theory. The beauty-pageant culture of the South reinforces male sexist attitudes towards women. Southern women are expected to have their hair washed and their makeup on and look good at all times, not just on Sunday mornings in the Baptist Church so the Randy's in the balcony can ogle them.

Unlike those feisty ladies on the television show *Designing Women*, the typical Southern belle is likely to be light years behind her Northern counterpart when it comes to not tolerating sexist male behavior. When we listen to those *Designing Women* we're really listening to producer Linda Bloodworth Thomason, or perhaps her friend Hillary Rodham Clinton; hardly your average "Bubbettes" in the rural South. If the beauty-pageant culture has taught Southern women anything, it is to try to look appealing to their men rather than confront them. Southern girls are brought up to be submissive. If Bubba likes to "git tore up," then Bubbette is likely to be right there with him or else has resigned herself to accepting that "it's just the way Bubba gets. He's just lettin' off steam. I'm not gonna try and change him." In other words: boys will be boys.

The alcohol problem is especially acute on college campuses. It's a nationwide problem, but here in the South, it's completely out of control. A colleague recently told me that a student dropped by his office to apologize for missing his Tuesday morning class. "I had to go to the emergency room to have my stomach pumped," she told him. "I chugged eight cans of beer on an empty stomach and got alcohol poisoning."

"Do you realize you could have killed yourself?" my colleague replied.

"Yes, Sir," she said. Southern co-eds are usually very polite, as submissive as puppy dogs, whether they take you seriously or not.

When I passed this story along to my friends in the fitness club they doubted its accuracy. "She's lying," Lance said. "You won't get alcohol poisoning from just eight beers."

I said, "But you have to remember, Lance, that women usually weigh a lot less than men. She probably only weighed 100 pounds or so. That's a lot of alcohol on an empty stomach. And anyway, what's a college student doing partying on a Monday night?"

Lance said, "What's wrong with Monday night?"

Randy said, "If you think those co-eds are there to listen to your boring geography lectures, Allan...get real, man! They're there to party!"

Randy got stopped at a road block on the way home from the Carolina football game last weekend. The highway patrolman shined his flashlight into Randy's car and spotted two empty beer cans on the floor of the passenger side where Randy was sitting. Randy wasn't driving, but the patrolman asked him to get out of the car. Randy's friend, Gary, was the designated driver that day, but South Carolina now has an open container law. Randy got fined 110 dollars. He said, "That $7.99 case of Genuine Draft cost me $117.99! And I wasn't even driving! That's the kicker! Here I played it safe and got a designated driver, and I still got busted! I should have tossed the empties out the window. The law's screwed up. I didn't want to litter, but the way the law is now, it encourages people to litter. I guess from now on I'm going to have to be more careful."

"You mean, you're not going to drink on the way to and from Carolina games anymore?" I said.

"Yeah, right." Randy said. "But you know, I did luck out. I was standing there, drunker n' a skunk and babbling to that cop, and all that time I had my dope in my pants pocket! The cop says, "Y'all been to the game?" I said, "Oh, yeah," and I started tellin' him all about it. Ol' Gary, he leaned out the car window and said, "Man, will you shut up!" I mean, I was doin' a lot of talking; I was really messed up. But let me tell ya', those cops had this big ol' nigger in the police cruiser, and they had him handcuffed to the door! You know, I felt sorry for that ol' nigger. He wasn't any drunker than I was and they were haulin' his butt off to jail!"

1993

8

BASKETBALL MEMORIES — ON BEING A "DUB"

Basketball is hardly one of my passions. Except for three very lonely and miserable winters as a most reluctant and unlikely "fan" at Sumner Memorial High School in the late 1960s, I've rarely paid any attention to the sport. In fact, I haven't seen a basketball game, either live or on television, since my college days in the early 1970s.

I began this essay — mentally, at least — more than a year ago, only to abandon it when the Beals-Hyde controversy flared up in the Maine newspapers. I had been wanting to get down on paper the painful memories of my high school basketball years, in hopes that I might initiate a constructive dialogue on the mission of interscholarstic sports, but decided that emotions were just too high.

This is written in part for all the "dubs," which in my high school days was what you were labeled by your peers if you weren't much of an athlete, especially a basketball player.

Basketball was everything when I attended Sumner High School. Being a dub at Sumner might have been OK if I had always been a dub, but for me it was especially excruciating because I had never been one; on the contrary, I had been a standout athlete at my large suburban junior high in New Jersey.

My father had died suddenly on vacation in Maine during July 1966, and my mother and I moved from New Jersey to Steuben later that summer.

I couldn't wait to move to Maine. I hated New Jersey. It was too densely populated, too money-oriented, too status-conscious. There were too many petty rules and regulations. You couldn't even light a firecracker or carry around a BB gun. My parents and I had spent two or three precious weeks vacationing in Maine each summer, and now suddenly my mother and I were going to be permanent residents. I remember that the awful grief I had felt from my father's untimely passing was at least somewhat ameliorated that summer by my mother's decision to move to Maine. But then I went to Sumner High School.

In New Jersey, physical education had been my favorite class. We ran laps, played football and soccer in the fall; lifted weights, practiced tumbling and gymnastics, and wrestled in the winter; and played baseball, softball, and ran track in the spring. I excelled at them all and was one of the fastest boys in the school in the 60-yard dash.

My first day at Sumner, the physical education teacher simply threw out two basketballs. What's this? I wondered. The boys in my class couldn't wait to choose sides; that is, all except me and a couple of pale-faced doughboys. I'd never played this game. I recall trying awkwardly to dribble the big round ball over to the basket, where I stopped short, and with both feet planted flat on the floor I sort of tossed the ball clumsily upward in the direction of the hoop. I missed. Everyone laughed. So did I — but inside, I was crying. A layup! I hadn't the foggiest idea how to execute a simple layup!

I suppose I was at least vaguely aware of black kids in the New Jersey ghettos of Newark and Patterson playing basketball on concrete courts; but in the all white middle-class suburbs where I grew up, the major winter sport was then — and still is — wrestling. All of our gymnastics, running, and weight-training were to prepare us for wrestling. Wrestlers were the gods of suburban New Jersey high schools.

By ninth grade, I had become a pretty good wrestler. My wrestling career — or so I had thought — was just beginning. But what I really excelled at was rope climbing. I was like an ape, or a teenaged Tarzan. I could scamper up a 16-foot rope in four seconds flat. Four seconds! It's no wonder my P.E. instructors, all of whom had biceps like grapefruits and had graduated from prestigious Springfield College, thought I had the potential to become a varsity wrestler.

I'll never forget Coach Buck. He was short; about 5 feet 6, with a barrel chest, bulging biceps, a bull neck, and a blocky head with a burr cut. "Wipe that smirk off your face!" he bellowed at the scrawny, bookish kid alongside me as we strained at our pushups. "Your arms look like two strings hanging there! And you want to be a wrestler? Hah!"

A wrestler! I laugh hysterically when I think back on it now; just like I laugh when I recall being a dub at Sumner High. What did it matter? But to a 15-year-old boy who had lived and breathed sports since the age of 5, to suddenly go from an up-and-coming wrestler whom everyone respected to a "useless" dub was devastating. I had been a "big man" at my suburban New Jersey junior high; at tiny Sumner High School in East Sullivan, Maine, I was nobody. So I withdrew into my own world. I'd ride the school bus home, grab my shotgun or .22 rifle and disappear into the woods, where I spent nearly all of my free time. I loved the Maine woods and water — still do — and gradually became aware of plants and trees, rocks and landforms, weather and climate, wildlife and marine resources, and the people who harvested them. So while my classmates were sweating it out in the gym, I was out in the elements, trying to keep from freezing; but in the process, getting a more pensive and solitary education — perhaps even sowing the seeds of my eventual career as a geographer.

I did earn varsity letters at baseball and cross country at Sumner, so naturally I was expected to participate in the activities of the Varsity Club. So during home basketball games I worked in the school kitchen, cooking and selling hot dogs, potato chips, and sodas to the fans. I didn't care to travel to the away games, and since I missed all the home games because I was working at the concession stand, I never acquired an interest in or an understanding of the game. Surprisingly, my P.E. teacher never bothered to teach us the fundamentals of basketball either. Evidently, he just assumed you would know how to play by the time you got to high school. Or perhaps he saw no point in wasting his time with dubs. Too bad.

What I did learn from high school basketball, however, was humility. I might have been a letterman at Sumner, but baseball and cross country were minor sports compared to basketball. And since the cross country meets and baseball games were always held in the afternoon, hardly any spectators ever came out. But it seemed as if the whole town traveled over to East Sullivan for basketball games. And like the wrestlers of suburban New Jersey, the "Sumner Boys" were treated like "gods" in the school and surrounding communities.

I soon learned that all the good-looking girls at Sumner were already spoken for. I never had a date until near the end of my senior year, and even then I lacked the courage — indeed, the "audacity" — to even approach one of the elite girls. "She's already taken," my dub friends would warn. Sumner High, I quickly learned, was a closed society, open only to the basketball clique. They were the elite. I didn't fit in. I didn't want to fit in. I got so tired of hearing about basketball that I really didn't give a rip whether they won or lost. Actually, I secretly reveled when they lost, as it temporarily knocked them off their high horses.

Nevertheless, by the time I graduated from Sumner I'd made many friends, many of whom I still keep up with. My best friends were mostly dubs themselves — some of them real dubs, the pale-skinned doughboys who didn't participate in any sports. But did it really matter? If anything, going from being a big jock in New Jersey to a useless dub in Maine made me a kinder, more sensitive person. It knocked me down a peg or two, made me realize we can't all be jocks; nor should we aspire to be. We all have our special abilities and talents, and these should be pursued and cultivated regardless of whether they are deemed important in the local popular culture.

There's nothing wrong with being a dub; we're all dubs at certain things anyway. What is harmful, in my view, is placing too much emphasis on varsity sports. Whether it's football in the South, wrestling in the mid-Atlantic States, or basketball in Maine or Indiana, varsity athletics are often foolishly overemphasized, leaving a lot of less talented youngsters — kids in dire need of fun, fitness, and camaraderie — out in the cold. Indeed, numerous studies have recently shown that in spite of our sports-crazed culture, the majority of today's youth in Maine and elsewhere are in sorry physical condition — flabbier even than their peers of 20 years ago. What difference is there between being a coach potato or a bleachers potato anyway? We need to be encouraging participation, not elitism. While there's certainly nothing wrong with celebrating athletic excellence, our obsession with producing winning teams and athletic programs that provide entertainment for the community may inadvertently be encouraging elitism at the expense of participation. Which is better? I suppose it's a matter of opinion. Personally, I'd rather see a hundred youngsters of all different levels of ability participating in a variety of athletics than a hundred zealous fans madly cheering a handful of elite athletes.

So as another Maine high school basketball season gets into full swing, my sympathies go out to all you dubs. Take heart. There is life after high school basketball. The season will be over before you know it...and it's not all that important anyway.

1994

9

REDNECKS

One damp overcast Saturday in March when I was running along a country road about five miles from my home in Marion, South Carolina, a big old car approached me slowly from the west with three forms in the front seat. The car was poking along at 35 to 40 miles an hour on a road where most people drive 60. When the car — an old 98 Olds — slowed, three men in the front seat simultaneously saluted by holding up three pints of whiskey. They grinned real big. I smiled and waved. Then I started laughing. Rednecks! Deep woods rednecks, they're called locally.

Now I'm not one to condone drinking and driving, but the image of those three 40-something white males with their pints of whiskey at four o'clock on a Saturday afternoon brought me instant joy. In this age of self-help books, co-dependency groups, tell-all talk shows, touchy-feeliness, and political correctness, there are still a few good ol' boys out there who'll do as they damn well please. They're not gonna change either. No matter how many laws are passed, the American redneck is going to break his share of them.

I like rednecks. Some of my best friends are rednecks. They're friends I can count on, too. They're honest, hardworking, straightforward, and patriotic. And they're predictable; I always know where they stand. Most rednecks will give you the shirt off their back.

Rednecks are found in every state, but they're especially common in the South, the West, the Midwest, north and south Jersey, the Bronx, Long Island, upstate New York, Massachusetts, Connecticut, Rhode Island, Vermont, New Hampshire, and of course, Maine. Maine, in particular, has some of the best rednecks in America. I don't think there's a town in the whole state of Maine that doesn't have its share of 'em, either. About the only places in Maine where rednecks are hard to find are the Grand Auditorium in Ellsworth and maybe the Left Bank Cafe in Blue Hill. Although I'd be willing to bet that some of those ponytailed, Saab-driving, organic farmer types are closet rednecks. Deep down, I'll bet they'd rather be at the stockcar races guzzling Miller Genuine Draft than out in the pasture shoveling sheep manure.

Stockcar racing is one of the last bastions of the American redneck. As my friend Randy explained to me recently, "Looky here, Allan, you ain't gonna find many niggers or sandniggers at the stockcar races...just real American-type people."

"Sandniggers?"

"Sandniggers — Mexicans, A-rabs, Gooks, Would-be's, Fuzzy-Wuzzys, whatever...Sandniggers...anybody who ain't real niggers or real American-type people."

"American-type people?"

"People like me or Denny."

"What about me?"

"Got-tall-mighty! Allan, you're a Yankee. Ain't nothin' lower than a Yankee, 'cept maybe an old redneck like Morgan Shepherd." Randy knows I'm a Morgan Shepherd man. He's my favorite NASCAR driver. Actually, I don't know a thing about him; I just like the sound of his name.

Most rednecks don't like minorities or outsiders all that much. David, my mechanic, is another example. Whenever David works on my car he offers to drive me home even though I live across town. But that's just the way he is; he's generous with his time. One day, as we were getting into his Cadillac, an elderly black man rode by on a bicycle. David turned to me and said, "I don't give a damn about a got-damned nigger." Well, I didn't know quite how to respond. I said, "Well, you know, David, there's good and bad people of every race." David said, "Most niggers is messed up." Those weren't his exact words, of course, but he wanted me to know he didn't like blacks.

But I had also noticed how David treated his black customers — with respect. He said, "Yes Sir" and "Yes Ma-am." And he didn't keep them waiting or ignore them either. He listened to them when they had a problem, and then he tried to fix it.

Southern rednecks may be racists, but I also believe they understand black people and their problems better than those well-educated politically correct urbanites who act horrified whenever they hear someone use the word nigger. In South Carolina I've heard nigger used a lot in public, but only by black men who affectionately refer to one another as niggers. Rednecks use the word among themselves, but rarely in public, or in the presence of blacks. In fact, my redneck friends in South Carolina didn't use the word in front of me until they had known me quite well — or, until we had become good friends.

Southern rednecks understand blacks because they often live and work right alongside them. They have for generations. Most Southern rednecks are working-class folks who can't afford to live in upscale all-white neighborhoods. They've grown up living and working with blacks, and there is a mutual respect between the two races. Each knows what sort of behavior is within bounds, which imaginary cultural boundaries you can or cannot cross; therefore, Southern rednecks and blacks coexist peacefully.

My friend Denny is a good ol' boy. The truth is, none of my friends would be considered rednecks — far from it — they're good ol' boys. There's quite a difference and it has taken me many years — much enlightenment — to understand the subtleties of rural Southern culture. Quite often I still don't get it.

Denny makes big bucks at the paper mill. He drives a $35,000 Ford Explorer with an Eddie Bauer interior. He also lives in a very nice home in the affluent English Park neighborhood. Denny often describes his buddy, Marcel, who is black, as "that big ol' nigger boy who works at the mill." Like me, Denny and Marcel are runners too. Except lately, Marcel has been beating both of us in the local races. Denny will say to me, "Son, that ol' nigger, Marcel, can run now." Yet, whenever Denny and I go to a race together, the first person Denny wants to see is Marcel. They shake hands, slap each other on the back, they joke and banter back and forth. I'm always amazed at the affection they lavish on each other. Because as soon as Denny gets back among his white buddies, Marcel becomes "that big ol' nigger boy at the mill" again.

A colleague from North Carolina explained it to me this way, "You've got to realize, Allan, that three things matter most to your typical southern white man — his car, his race, and his religion."

I used to worry that as the United States became more urbanized and homogenized rednecks would become an endangered species. But not any more; on the contrary, I think the American redneck will outlast the common cockroach. History is on his side. As any redneck will tell you, any Americans that have ever amounted to anything, like Elvis, for example, have been rednecks or else aspired to be rednecks. We've even had rednecks in the White House. Andrew Jackson was one. They say ol' Hickory stank so bad you couldn't get within 10 yards of him. More recently, George Bush Sr. said he didn't like broccoli, but liked to eat pork rinds; and, depending on the audience, seemed almost to aspire to be a redneck. But he just couldn't seem to get the hang of it. He even lived in Texas, a state with more rednecks than rattlesnakes. Between winters in Texas and summers in Maine, you'd have thought George Bush would have been the Redneck President instead of just the Education and Environment President.

Finally, I think Bill Clinton would like very much to be a redneck too, but the real rednecks don't want any part of him. You see, rednecks are nearly always Republicans. When Bill Clinton appeared at Darlington Motor Speedway a couple of years ago, all the good ol' boys stood up and booed.

1995

10

THINKING MOTORCYCLES: A MID-LIFE CRISIS?

"You sound just like you did when I first met you...always talking about motorcycles...you're acting like an excited teenager again."

That's what my wife, Linda, said to me the other night while we waited in the drive-thru line at Wendy's. I was 18 when I first met Linda. I had ridden a 350cc Yamaha motorcycle 1,800 miles from my home in Steuben to college in southern Arkansas that fall. Two years later, in 1971, I sold the bike and bought an old Volvo. I haven't ridden a motorcycle in nearly 25 years.

But like some mysterious, recurring fever, the bike mania has suddenly returned. It first struck in late August. That's when I started visiting the Honda, Kawasaki, and Yamaha dealerships in Florence, South Carolina, and in Lumberton, North Carolina. I kept thinking it would pass. I'd get all worked up about bikes; then, after a night's sleep, I'd come to my senses in the morning. I'd say to Linda, "I must be going crazy! Surely this is gonna pass. Once the cooler weather comes I'll forget all about motorcycles."

I guess I'm having a mid-life crisis. Only...I'm perfectly content with my lot in life. In fact, I think I'm happier right now than I have been in years. Indeed, once the bike fever struck, I was suddenly oblivious to anything that might make me unhappy. I was simply bike-crazy.

"I'm gonna beat this thing," I kept saying to Linda. But no matter how determined I was to whip it, the bug kept coming back.

"Oh, it won't go away." That's what my friend, Teddy, assured me. Teddy rides a 1340cc Harley Davidson Fatboy —- an $18,000 machine. Teddy wouldn't be caught dead riding "Japanese metal" — one of those "rice burners" or "crotch rockets."

It was Teddy who suggested we ride up to Lumberton, North Carolina one Saturday morning to look at the Hondas at Currie's Chainsaw and Cycle Shop. Teddy had bought his very first bike, a 350cc Honda, there in 1968. Teddy owns a heating and air-conditioning business now. He works hard. He has several employees and a big payroll to make each week. He needed a Saturday diversion.

That's the wonderful thing about bike fever — it really is a diversion. Any other autumn I would have paid attention to the O.J. Simpson trial, the war in Bosnia, the possible balkanization of Canada, or to problems and politics at the university where I teach. But not this year; I'm completely out of it. When Teddy and I talk about bikes, it's as if all the world's problems suddenly vanish. The machine is all that matters. Motorcycles are the ultimate form of escapism. Whether you're riding or just looking at them, motorcycles have the power to take you into another state of mind.

The weather finally turned cool. One morning, I said to Linda, "You see this! I'm throwing away all these brochures on the Yamaha bikes. That's the end of it! I'm all done!" I was in the kitchen, hovering over the trash dispenser. I'd had bad dreams all night — nightmares about motorcycles that wouldn't start, motorcycles that broke down and left me stranded in dark and dangerous places. What was I doing there? Where was I trying to go?

I tossed and turned; I struggled and strained and pushed the heavy machine down the road; but still, it wouldn't crank. I was miles from home, lost in some swampy, redneck trailer ghetto, with the sun sinking fast, the German Shepherds and Rotweilers charging and the bike dead.

I woke up exhausted. I felt foolish. I said to Linda, "The last thing I need is a motorcycle. It's only going to make my life more complicated. More anxiety. More frustration. Who needs it? This is the end. It's all over!"

Linda just looked at me in pity and said, "I don't think it's over."

That evening, I quietly fished the Yamaha brochures out of the garbage. A couple of days later, I stopped by the Motor Vehicle Department and picked up a copy of the motorcycle operator's manual. I started carrying the booklet around in my briefcase, pulling it out when I got bored with my work and studying on the sly.

It will pass. I know I'll get over it.

But why, after 25 years, do I suddenly think I need a motorcycle again? What happens to men when they get into their mid-40s? I know my hair is thinning and turning gray; still, I don't feel any different than I did 25 years ago. I'm still the same weight.

It's something else; memories that seem to be slipping away; memories I want, somehow, to resurrect, yet I know I really can't go back to that time and place. But maybe if I got on a machine again I could bring back that magical period in my life. I could reenter a world of roads not taken.

It was the year I met Linda; and the world that I entered as a college freshman, thousands of miles from home, seems almost like a dream now. So long ago; so many things change in a quarter of a century. If only I could just fly back in time and see it all again, if only for a day or two.

And I still remember the power of the throttle, the feel of the wind in my face and the sense of freedom the bike gave me. I was an outlaw on that machine. I was Marlon Brando, John Wayne, or whoever I wanted to be, riding off into the sunset. I remember that when I arrived on campus in Arkansas, I didn't want to stay; I just wanted to get back on the bike and keep riding. I telephoned my mother. She told me to stay put, to give it a chance.

I saw things on that bike too. The colors of the landscape seemed more vivid, the cold and the rain more fierce and immediate, the smells and sounds more stimulating. No wonder I became a geography professor.

On the machine, rather than in an automobile, you feel every contour of the land; you see and experience geography in a way you can never experience it in a car. I've never liked cars; never cared anything about them. I've never even made a car payment. I always buy some half worn-out clunker, then drive it 'til it croaks. A motorcycle, though, is a vessel of spare beauty. It's sleek and elegant. I'm content to just stare at them and smile, as if I were admiring a precious work of art.

"That's it," I assured Linda. "Maybe all I need to do is look at bikes now and then. I probably don't really want one; I need to just stop by the bike shops every so often and just sit on a machine."

But then one day recently, I found myself seriously inquiring about a used Yamaha 535 Virago.

"Uh, could I try it out?" I asked the salesman.

"Do you have a motorcycle license?"

"Uh, no."

"Okay. Well, we'll just get one of the boys out back to give you a ride on 'er."

"Uh, yeah. Uh, that would be great." My heart started pounding. I had only ridden on the back of a motorcycle once before. It scared the living daylights out of me. It is one thing to ride the bike yourself; it is quite another to hang on for your life while some gearhead rides you around.

"Are you ready?" A young man — he might have been 18 — approached me with an extra helmet in his hand. It was one of those space-age models that wraps around your whole head and neck, leaving just a small opening for your eyes, nose, and mouth. A clear, plastic visor flipped down over the opening.

"Take it easy on me," I pleaded. "I haven't been on one of these things in more than 20 years."

He just grinned at me and said, "I don't guess we'll fall. I ain't never rode one of these here Viragos before!" Gulp.

A log truck was bearing down on us as we eased out of the Yamaha dealership. At that moment, I thought: what an absolutely dumb way to end my life! But my driver gunned the engine and off we went, across the median and into the opposite lane. When he had gotten the machine up to about 60 mph, I hollered, "It seems to run just fine. That's good enough for me!" He made a couple of wicked turns, cruised around a subdivision, bounced us over a speed bump and roared back on to the highway. I was definitely shaking when I got off that machine. But I could barely contain my huge smile...of joy...and relief.

"Oh, yeah! It runs great!" I said.

No doubt the salesman was already seeing dollar signs. But I'm just not an impulsive person. On the contrary, I'm a salesman's worst nightmare. Of course, I had no intention of buying the bike; at least, not at that very moment. I'd think it over, I said. I'd have to discuss it with Linda. I'd get back to him later. Of course, I never did.

What was I thinking about? Why did I even go on that test drive? Did I just get caught up in the moment? Or was I hoping that the ride would scare me enough so that I would forget all about motorcycles? Perhaps it was to remind me of how windy it gets on a motorcycle and how exposed you are to the elements. Or maybe it was to help me realize something that was hard for me to fathom as a fearless teenager: how dangerous motorcycles really are. That's the end of it, I thought, as I got into my car and drove off.

It wasn't. A couple of days ago, I went to the Motor Vehicle Department, took the written test, and got my learner's permit. Now all I need is a bike.

Maybe I can learn something about America and about myself by riding a motorcycle again. Maybe there is something out there that can only be gotten through the simplicity of the machine.

But the weather is really turning chilly now. And the early darkness encourages one to come in out of the cold and put one's thoughts down on paper. Indeed, the act of writing is, itself, a form of therapy. So maybe...the fever will pass.

1995

11

MY LOVE AFFAIR WITH RUNNING

I went to Charlotte, North Carolina, on February 17 to run my 47th marathon. It was also the site of the 1996 Men's Olympic Trials race. And while I knew I had no chance of making the U.S. Olympic team, it was still a thrill and a privilege to run the same 26-mile, 385-yard course as the Olympians.

It was cold — 25 degrees and very windy. We'd had snow showers in the Carolinas the Friday before the race. At one point, the snow was coming down so hard I wondered if my wife, Linda, and I would even make it up to Charlotte, but it cleared out by Saturday morning. I emerged from the Charlotte Convention Center just five minutes before the start of the race. I was nervous — pre-race jitters! And I had another problem: the starting line had been moved from its usual place. I suddenly realized I had no idea where the race was to begin. What does a runner do in 25-degree weather, wearing only running shorts, long-sleeved T-shirt, cap and gloves? Well, run of course. I got directions, and a breathless half-mile later, I was uptown near the old convention center, climbing over a high metal fence, then making a leap of faith into the throng of anxious runners. Bang! I just made it.

I ran exactly 3,500 miles in 1995. Two weeks or so before the end of December, after I had totaled up my mileage for the year to date, I made it my goal to run exactly 3,500 miles. It wasn't my best year, but a good one — a marathon in April, a handful of shorter races, six weeks of mostly high altitude running while on sabbatical in Mexico, and — at age 44 — no injuries. Luck!

My hottest run was a seven miler in 102-degree heat on August 14 in Marion, South Carolina. My coldest run was probably the January morning I ran eight miles at 8,700 feet elevation in Toluca, Mexico. I can still remember the smell of the diesel buses as I sucked in the rarefied air. My longest day of 1995 was the day I left Mexico. I ran seven miles at sunrise in Mexico City, then got the scare of my life when my Atlanta-bound plane had problems with its landing gear. That night, I ran another seven miles in Marion, South Carolina. After six weeks of traveling alone in Mexico, that evening jog was my happiest run of 1995. It might have been the happiest of my life.

I guess you'd have to call me a runner's runner. I have neither speed nor talent, only endurance plus a lifelong love of movement that has kept me running marathons the past 27 years. And that was the history I carried with me to Charlotte. I've never won a race. I'm only getting slower, and my gait has gotten so awkward that locals refer to me as "that gimpy-legged old man who runs all over the place."

I don't know if it's possible to explain the appeal of marathon running to non-runners. I guess people think I'm some sort of masochist. But really, if it hurt that much, would I want to do it 47 times? Well, definitely. Actually, the pain comes on so subtly, you hardly even realize you're hurting until perhaps the 11th or 12th mile. By the halfway point in a marathon, you know you're in a race. And during that second half, as you look for each successive mile marker, you become more and more focused, until about three or four miles from the end you've blocked out everything else in your life: getting to the finish is all that matters. The world around you ceases to exist. You're a zombie. It's you and that road. This is what it has all come down to — you've pared your life to the bone. I know it means nothing to anyone else. But for me, and for anyone who has ever run a marathon, the experience has no equal.

I've been in love with the idea of marathon running since I was 15. That was when I first read about the Boston Marathon in Sports Illustrated. Two years later, when I was 17, I falsified my date of birth on my entry form and ran the Boston Marathon in three hours and 58 minutes.

At Charlotte, the icy wind cut through my thin cotton T-shirt like a cold steel knife. But whenever we turned a corner and the wind was at our backs, the sun felt warm — so warm that I threw away my gloves and chugged plenty of water and Gatorade at the aid stations. Experience! I once passed out in a hot marathon in Galveston, Texas, and have gotten leg cramps in several other marathons. Experience has taught me to fear dehydration more than anything else. Apparently it did the same for Bob Kempainen, the eventual winner of the Charlotte Marathon. He was vomiting his guts out the last three miles. Was the temperature so low that he couldn't get the fluid down? Who knows? I had the opposite problem: I drank so much that I had to make a brief pit stop at nine miles. That's still better than risking dehydration, hypothermia, stroke, and possibly death. There are occasionally deaths in marathons — recent Marine Corps and New York City races come to mind.

You never know how your body is going to respond to heat, cold, hills, or wind. The race is just too long; there are no guarantees that you are going to be able to finish the marathon, no matter how many miles you have trained. But on this day in Charlotte, something unusual happened to me: I got faster. Between 14 and 19 miles, I speeded up. People started coming back to me. I was having a good day.

On Saturday and Sunday afternoons between October and April, I enjoy going on 15- to 20-mile runs in all sorts of weather. Those long solitary weekend runs are my winter ritual. I don't watch any football or sports on television. I just go out and enjoy the oak-pine-woods and the solitude. I think. I work things out in my head. And as the sun sinks and the chill comes on, these winter runs are as close as I can get to slowing down my life and savoring the moment.

Marathon running really is a single-minded and, perhaps, selfish pursuit. In order to run 3,500 miles in 1995, I had to average 67 miles per week, or about an hour and twenty minutes a day. The winner of this race probably averages 150 miles a week. We all have our priorities: I don't hunt and seldom fish; I don't play golf or tennis or sail a boat.

I've always wanted to be a marathon runner. This is what I remind myself as I approach the 20th mile. I'm hurting. I am no longer able to wave or smile at the kind people who line the course and have taken the time to look up my number and call out my name. I appreciate them. I really do. But I'm slowly dying. Knives are being driven into my thighs — Charlotte is hilly, with bone-crunching downhills — and my left calf feels like it wants to cramp.

In 1969, when I was 17 and attempting my first Boston Marathon, a savior came to my rescue. I'll never forget him. I'll never forget his face or the sound of his voice. He might have been the age I am now. I had quit. I had stopped running. I was sitting on the curb with nine miles left to run. I had taken off my left shoe. My foot was blistered. Blood coated my sock. I wondered why I had been so foolish as to think I could do this thing, run this marathon. Then I heard his voice.

"Come on, Allan! I know you can do it!"

Ghostlike runners silently shuffled by. They were moving forward. That's what it had all come down to for them: simply moving forward.

I looked up, looked into this stranger's eyes. Why had this smartly-dressed, middle-aged man bothered to come over and encourage me, a teenage boy from Sumner High School in East Sullivan, Maine? He knew, of course, that this was a crucial moment in one of the most important days of my young life. After all, I had gotten up the courage to come to Boston to run with the world's best. Did I really want to quit? I'd have to face my classmates at Sumner and hear, "I told you so." I looked at him and said...nothing. I put my shoe back on, got up, and did what those other, ghostlike runners were doing: I moved forward.

"Lo puedo hacer! I can do it!" I said to myself in Spanish as I approached the 23rd mile in Charlotte. Whenever I've been alone in Mexico, in moments of weakness or insecurity, that's what I've said, again and again. I wanted this, now here I am. I can do it! So much of life is about forcing yourself to do things you're really not sure you can do. You have doubts, second thoughts. You begin to wonder if this is what you really wanted in life. What am I doing here? Why am I doing this? But do you really want to settle for something less than you can be?

I finished 70th out of 1,300 or so runners at Charlotte in three hours and 12 minutes. Bob Kempainen of Minnetonka, Minnesota, was the winner of the Olympic Trials race in two hours and 12 minutes. Kempainen got $100,000 for his effort. All I got for my extra hour of pain was a finisher's medal, a T-shirt, and a space blanket to wrap around my shivering body. It was all I expected.

I was so cold at the finish that I never even stopped, never even sat down to catch my breath. Linda and I walked the half-mile to where we had parked the car. I toweled off, put on a sweater and we drove the three hours back home to Marion, South Carolina.

I don't know what Bob Kempainen did the day after the marathon, but I jogged five miles — to work the soreness out. The next day I ran seven and, by the following weekend, I was back to my long solitary running through the piney woods.

1996

12

TRUSTFUNDLANDIA

This summer I made a discovery. If you have to go into Ellsworth and you want an authentic Maine experience, then go to Wal-Mart.

To me, people make a place, and Wal-Mart feels more like Maine than any other store in Ellsworth. The people who work at Wal-Mart are helpful, courteous and pleasant — and they're actually from Maine and so are most of the customers. At least they were in June, the last time I made it up to that sprawling strip-mall of a city. I'm afraid I've fallen out of love with Ellsworth, MDI and the Blue Hill area. In recent years, I've become less and less tolerant of the catastrophic cultural upheaval that has occurred in that part of Hancock County. I'm simply tired of artists, craftspeople, gourmet cooks, musicians, organic farmers, mountain bikers, potters, weavers, winemakers, writers, kayakers, yachtspeople and everything else that is trendy in this so-called "Downeast Maine." I know I'm a curmudgeon, but I'm just tired of reading about all these Ivy League-educated, trust fund babies that come to Maine and make bells and baskets and jams and jellies and wooden boats, wines and whatnot, call themselves Maine artists, then charge prices for this stuff that nobody in Maine (but them) could afford.

It was for all those reasons that I recently made a journey up Route 2 to Lincoln, Maine. I had some idea of Lincoln from the story about the young soldier from there who had died heroically in Somalia. So I got it into my head that if there was any place left in Maine that was not overrun with B&Bs that charge $100 a night, and fancy restaurants that serve expensive wines and skimpy overpriced gourmet meals featuring strange sauces I'd never heard of and couldn't pronounce, that Lincoln might just be the place.

It was.

The folks up in Lincoln were down-to-earth and pleasant. There are few tourists and transplants. You get the impression that most people in Lincoln were born and raised there. The restaurants are a lot cheaper than the ones Down East — even more reasonable than the restaurants in the "other state of Maine," Washington County. The portions are also larger in Lincoln, a milltown, where people work hard and have big appetites. The restaurant where I ate even featured genuine American wines by Ernest and Julio Gallo.

Go ahead and sneer if you want. But do we really need a $20 bottle of Chardonnay to enhance a meal? Why do we have to be such elitists down on the coast? It wasn't always that way. Think back to the time when E.B. White first came here. Why did he choose this place? Would he have chosen it now? He probably would have bought a farm in Lincoln instead.

The waitress told me that people in Lincoln were real worried about the possible ban on clearcutting. "Oh, it would kill this town." When I told her that I had graduated from Sumner Memorial High School in East Sullivan, and now summered in Gouldsboro, she said, "Oh, I've lived in several places down on the coast — Trenton, Ellsworth, Franklin and Blue Hill.

"Oh, it was awful. Terrible. Snobs. You'd be standing in line at the supermarket and they'd talk right over you — like you wasn't even there."

"Yeah, I guess they've driven most of the Maine people away," I joked.

"Really. Well, I thought Franklin was still pretty nice. That wasn't too bad, yet."

I asked her how many people lived in Lincoln.

"About 5,000."

"About like Ellsworth."

"Except that Ellsworth has about 25,000 in the summer," she added, with a laugh.

"So you're back home now?" I asked.

"Yep. My husband and I were in Guam when he was in the service, but we're home now."

"No place like home," I added.

"Really."

While in Lincoln, I went to the Wal-Mart store there and had the same positive experience I'd had in Ellsworth. Both the employees and customers made it feel very local. And when I asked an employee if they had a men's restroom, she stopped what she was doing and led me through the maze of aisles and right to it.

I also dropped by the local motorcycle dealership and came away wishing I'd bought my bike from those folks.

There was much about Lincoln that took me back to a Maine I remembered from the 1960s — no pretense, just genuine Maine people. I liked Lincoln. I plan to go back. In fact, I wouldn't mind living there for a while, just to get to know it better. I also think that people on the coast, in places like Blue Hill, could learn a lot about their state by visiting towns like Lincoln — it might be a mind-broadening experience.

On my way back to Gouldsboro, I stopped off in Ellsworth, at a trendy-sporting goods store. Lord, have mercy. Give me Wal-Mart any day. I've been an outdoor person all my life, but I swear I didn't know what half that stuff was. And expensive. And who were those people in there? And where did they get those strange new-age dialects that made me wince when I heard them say, "It's like really grrreen?" Where was I? California? I knew I wasn't in Lincoln, Maine. I'm not really sure I was even in Maine, as it certainly didn't look, sound, smell or feel like anything I was remotely familiar with.

And then it dawned on me. This was the feeling the waitress from Lincoln had when she lived in Blue Hill. If people make a place, and I'm certain they do, then these places really aren't Maine any more; they're some new, transformed space, that I'll just call Trustfundlandia, since hardly anyone there seems to have a traditional job — at least, the sort of job where you're held accountable to someone and you have to make a living, as you would in Lincoln or Franklin or in the other state of Maine — Washington County.

1996

THE OLDEST PATIENT

Our dog, Hallie, was the oldest patient at the Southland Animal Hospital in Mullins, South Carolina. Whenever we brought her in, our veterinarian would smile and cheerfully ask, "Well, how's Miss Hallie doin' today?" Everybody loved Hallie. She never knew an unkind word.

Hallie had known a half-dozen vets in her 16-year lifetime. She was a well-traveled dog, having lived in North Carolina, Colorado, North Dakota, and South Carolina, as well as summers in Maine. We had always hoped we could bury her on the property in West Gouldsboro, a place she dearly loved.

In 1981, the first summer we brought Hallie to Maine, she immediately took to life at the camp. She had never been swimming before, but the minute we threw a stick into Jones Pond, she waded right in and started paddling.

Hallie always knew when the long journey to Maine was over; she'd recognize the dirt road to the camp, remember where she was, and start barking. As soon as we opened the car door she'd come bounding out, wanting to run and play, and rediscover all her old haunts. She'd sneeze and snort, and get so excited we'd call her the "wild dog of the Pampa."

I'll always remember the end of Hallie's first summer. We had closed the camp and were carrying the last few items back to the car. Hallie just sat stubbornly in the path. She refused to move. We had to carry her to the car. She just didn't understand that life at the camp wasn't permanent.

I think we could have driven off without her. She seemed to be saying, "Okay, see you next summer, but I'm staying right here." I wanted to cry. I had felt as sad about leaving as she did. I always knew that dog had more sense than I'll ever have. Why were we leaving? For some stupid job?

I did cry this past August when we left Maine. I had taken one last look at Hallie's bed in the corner of the camp that morning, when my wife, Linda, asked, "What's the matter?" I just fell apart. We both knew it was Hallie's last summer.

When an old dog dies, you die a little yourself. It has been a month now since Hallie's passing, but I'm still not right. I keep expecting to see her lying in her favorite spot; I still find myself saving her those little tidbits from the table; I still wake up thinking I heard her bark, but there's nobody snoozing at my feet as I write these words. Nobody's waiting patiently when I go off to work, or to run, or to the grocery store. I loved my dog. I sometimes think I prefer dogs to humans. A whole part of my vocabulary left with Hallie — the silly names I called her, the strange phrases and codes I spoke in — I talked to her in a special language that only she owned.

Hallie brought out the best in me, especially near the end, when I had to help her up and down steps, and lift her up and steady her on her feet when she had to go out. She'd groan, and sometimes growl; she was doing the very best she could; still, I knew it frustrated her. Those hips and legs had gotten so stiff she could barely move. She'd bark during the night. I'd get out of bed repeatedly, and lift her to her feet so she could go round in her circle and get comfortable again. She'd been a great dog, a great runner that we called The Bullet Train, The Comet and Old Thunder. She'd run those tight circles that sheepdogs run. In fact, Hallie was always being mistaken for a Border Collie. She was black and white with long, soft fur.

I've never seen another dog quite like Hallie; she was a mixture of a sable collie and an English Setter. We found her in the classifieds of the *Charlotte Observer*. She was the best 20 dollars we've ever spent. And she was smart too — so intelligent that we had to spell around her.

By February of 1997, Hallie was blind and deaf and seldom able to get on her feet without assistance. And once she was up, she usually went down again. She just wanted to sleep, but she couldn't get comfortable. It became painful to watch her struggle. She'd always had a good appetite too, but we noticed that she was eating less, not to mention the many pills we had to force down her for various ailments.

And then one weekend she got a virus. The vet might have been able to clear it up, but watching her lie there in her misery, Linda and I had to ask ourselves if we were just keeping her going out of our own selfishness. She had a strong heart; she'd probably live on a little longer, but what sort of life does a dog have when it can't get up, or get comfortable, or even do its business without falling down?

The next day, I took Hallie to the vet for the last time. She weighed only 40 pounds; she had once weighed 54. I stroked Hallie's head, and said to the vet, "Well, after 16 years, she's finally calmed down."

The veterinarian smiled, and said, "Yeah, none of my dogs ever lived this long. Of course, you never spoiled her, did you?"

It barely took a minute...Hallie was gone.

Linda and I had been so sure it was time; still, I felt like I had murdered the best friend I ever had. Maybe we could have kept her going a little longer? Maybe we should have let her go much sooner? All we could do was bury her in the backyard and pray to God we did the right thing.

It's going to take us a very long time to get over Hallie's passing. She was our only child. But unlike children, who grow up and eventually leave home, dogs remain the same age intellectually. They're your little baby until...suddenly...they're gone. All you have are the memories.

A couple of weeks ago, on a farm high in the mountains near Asheville, North Carolina, a black and white Border Collie gave birth to a litter of pups. Next weekend, Linda and I are going to make the five-hour pilgrimage from the coastal plain to the Appalachians to have a look. It's springtime in the Carolinas; the dogwoods are blooming.

We know she won't be exactly like Hallie; but then, there could only be one Hallie. Still, maybe one of those puppies will give us that special sign. Maybe one of the females will come over and chew on my fingers the way Hallie once did, and announce that she is ours. She won't be ready to leave her mother just yet, so we'll have a little time to think it over. After all, she'll have to be able to run those tight circles. Hallie wouldn't have wanted anything less.

1997

14

THE WAY LIFE USED TO BE

My neighbor, who retired to Maine from Connecticut several years ago, recently said to me: "Allan, have you and Linda been thinking about the state of affairs in Maine this summer?" I had to smile. I knew what was coming next. Downeast Maine is not the same place it was five, or 10, or even two years ago. Places change. My neighbor has been especially upset this summer over the noise and annoyance of personal watercraft ("jet skis") on our pond, which is only 18 miles east of Ellsworth. He's even telephoned the local warden to see if anything can be done.

The summer sounds here at camp used to be birds singing, leaves rustling, and loons calling. Now we have the irritating whine of Ninja motorcycles on Route 1 early in the morning, followed by jet skis and speedboats plying the water all day long and sometimes into the night. The sirens of ambulances are, increasingly, common summer sounds too. We've had two young men killed on Route 1 in Gouldsboro the past two summers. The traffic is horrendous. People think I must have a death wish because I run along Route 1 between Gouldsboro and Sullivan every afternoon. But I've been running along this road for nearly 30 years, and unlike Routes 186 and 195, Route 1 at least has a wide shoulder.

Fortunately, change has come gradually to our little neighborhood. About 15 years ago, everybody on the north shore of the pond, except Linda and me, decided to get electricity.

I'm at a loss for words to express the sadness I felt the first time I saw those Bangor Hydro trucks come down our road. It's never been quite the same here. For several years after the arrival of the electricity, I had a recurring dream where I returned to our camp after a long absence only to find it surrounded by mobile homes.

But in 1997, our camp still has no electricity, running water, refrigeration, or telephone. It's still a camp. We still use an ice cooler, a tiny Coleman camping stove, kerosene lamps, a wood stove, and an outhouse. We may never get electricity. It would destroy the magic of the place. There would be no point in coming here anymore, because everything else around us has changed.

About five years ago, we arrived late one early June night, and...I swore I saw a red light in the sky. I had. It was a cellular phone tower, up in the woods across Route 1, barely a half-mile north of our camp. I walked down to the pond to fill a bucket of water that night, and across the pond I saw a second red light in the sky — another phone tower! The next day, Linda and I drove to Millbridge and saw a third tower to our east. We were surrounded by the darn things. All I could say was: "Nobody ever told us. Nobody even asked us our opinion. They just put those ugly things up and now we have to look at them."

And then, a few years ago, a man arrived on the dirt road leading to our camp, unloaded a backhoe, and after a few days, a gravel pit appeared in the meadow. Once there had been apple trees and blueberries and wild-flowers in the meadow; now, dump trucks rumble in and out periodically. Once I had seen a mother bear and two cubs; now, the hole in the earth just grows deeper and larger. It even has water in it...a local teenager has taken to sunbathing at the edge of the pit on hot summer afternoons. Who needs a pond anyway?

As a lover of motorcycles it is hard for me to find fault with the bikers on Route 1. And the gravel pit...well, people have to make a living. The jet skis really haven't bothered me much, either. Actually, it is kayaks that have been on my mind this summer. I am much bothered by what seems to be an explosion of kayaks — on top of cars, in ponds, lakes, bays, rivers and the ocean. Frankly, the kayaks scare me far more than the jet skis, the motorcycles, the dump trucks or the seasonal traffic.

Kayaks are clean, quiet; and if you use them properly, they're very safe. You can also go anywhere in them, and that's the problem. A friend of ours, who likes to sail, recently complained: "You can't go anywhere out in Frenchman Bay anymore without encountering these people in kayaks. They're crawling all over those islands. There's no place left out there that's untouched."

Indeed, kayaks are taking people to parts of Maine where humans have hardly trod — remote offshore islands, and ponds deep in the puckerbrush that are (were) still pristine. Bright green, orange, red and yellow kayaks; they're like floating plastic garbage, washing up on the incoming tide, transporting well-heeled, well-intentioned "adventure" tourists or "eco-tourists" to the last unspoiled paradises in Maine. These are "green" visitors treading lightly so as not to disturb the natural environment. But as geographer David Zurick has argued in his book, *Errant Journeys: Adventure Travel in a Modern Age*:

"The speed with which such changes occur can be remarkable. Tourists, especially adventure tourists, are keen to this and forever seek to visit a place 'before it is discovered and ruined.' For those same tourists to think they can somehow remove themselves from the process of ruination shows the power of the imagination — as if they could slip into and out of a place unnoticed."

But believe me, I notice them. We all do. We notice those gaudy plastic vessels on the tops of sport utility vehicles parked at L.L. Bean in Ellsworth. And I notice them when they nose around the lily pads in front of our camp. And as Professor Zurick suggests:

"It is only a matter of time before places become too commercialized for adventure purposes and are abandoned by the adventure agencies. At that point, the tourism product changes to one that appeals to less adventurous people, and pretty soon the place becomes simply another fabricated tourism spot enjoyed by ordinary holiday-makers."

I wonder, then, is the presence of the jet skiers on our pond an indication we have already lost much of what once made us so special? The jet skiers may be driving the kayakers away — sending them deeper into the Maine woods where they can "discover" some other "unspoiled" gem.

Meanwhile, Concord (Ellsworth) gets closer every day. The Ellsworth-Bar Harbor tourist corridor is spreading like cancer. And our little pond, just minutes from Ellsworth (in today's high-speed culture, as close in real time as Concord was to Walden Pond), seems destined to be devoured like Thoreau's beloved Walden.

1997

15

FALLING IN LOVE WITH WAL-MART

The other night at Wal-Mart here in Marion, South Carolina, I saw a middle-aged man approaching the checkout line with his big burly arms wrapped all around what must have been at least a half-dozen large bags of snacks — potato chips, pork rinds, cheez-balls, taco chips, seasoned popcorn, you name it. I thought to myself: now there's a happy man! You could see it in his face. He had a look of pure contentment, as if he had already died and gone to heaven. I was happy for him, too. I wanted, somehow, to be able to share in his joy.

I have to admit that I seem to be falling in love with Wal-Mart. I probably bop out there two or three nights a week — to check my blood pressure, to look at the people, the dog treats, tools, hardware, sporting goods, plants, shrubs, trees, garden supplies, even clothes.

My wife, Linda, recently asked me, "Allan, do you have anything but gray socks?"

"Uh, well, I think I still have one blue pair and a green pair." All the rest are these gray athletic socks that I keep buying at Wal-Mart. I just love those gray socks. I never wear anything but hiking boots or running shoes anyway, and I've decided I can simplify my life just a little bit by putting on gray socks every morning. That way, when I come home from work and change into my running clothes, I already have my socks on.

That's the beauty of Wal-Mart. I can get just about anything I need there. If I can't find it at Wal-Mart, I probably don't need it. I buy most of my shirts there, too. If I didn't buy the shirt at Wal-Mart, it must be one my sister gave me for Christmas. It's that simple.

It is also hard to go to Wal-Mart, either here in Marion, South Carolina, or in Ellsworth, Maine, without running into somebody I know. I'm always greeting friends and neighbors there; and, if I don't ever meet certain friends or neighbors there, I begin, inwardly, to wonder if they might be one of those people who just won't go to Wal-Mart. You know the type — they're trying to save small-town America; they're doing their part to help the little guy stay in business. Good for them! But they may also be paying higher prices. Actually, they're probably snobs who don't want to be seen at Wal-Mart. That's not me. Not at all. I like Wal-Mart because it's cheap. I can actually afford to buy a few things there.

Thanks to Wal-Mart, even a tightwad like me can become a consumer. I guess I'm also doing my part to keep the Industrial Revolution humming right along in the Third World. Hey, we've got a global economy now, and even I am a small part of it. I just wish they could pay those women who work in the electronics and apparel factories in Central America, China and elsewhere more than 56 cents an hour. That's the going wage in El Salvador. I'd gladly pay a little more for my gray socks if it would wind up in those women's paychecks rather than in some stockholder's portfolio. I'm for the little guy. I'm convinced the poor will inherit the earth.

I've been in Wal-Marts from South Carolina to Maine. I've also been to some of their stores out in Arkansas, where I once went to college. And you know what? Wal-Mart stores, though they are a big part of the homogenization of America, always have a very local ambience. The employees and the patrons tend to be natives of that town or immediate area. So if you want to meet native Arkansans, South Carolinians, or Mainers, then go to Wal-Mart.

Here in Marion, South Carolina, where more than half the population is black, Wal-Mart is primarily run and patronized by black people. And that's nice; it's as it should be. You can hear the local patois and bask in the local culture. Over in the automotive section, you can rub elbows with the local gearheads and perhaps learn the latest goings-on in the stock car racing scene. All of this is especially appealing to me because I've got to listen to long-winded college professors and airhead coeds all day long. Give me a bunch of good 'ol boys in a real American-type store like Wal-Mart for a change of pace.

One of my friends here said recently, "You know, Allan, when I retire, I think I'm gonna get me a part-time job out at Wal-Mart. I know a retired state trooper who works out there and he just loves it."

Actually, I wish there was no such thing as Wal-Mart, and that the world was as it was before the automobile and before the merchandising chains franchised America. I guess that's why I love little tiny country stores: they're relics from an age gone by, a pre-parking lot era when people still walked or rode horses and didn't have, or seem to need, the vast array of consumer goods modern society requires. The simple life: It is certainly something to aspire to. So perhaps a handful of inexpensive shirts and a drawer full of plain ol' gray socks is more than enough. It does it for me. See you at Wal-Mart.

1997

16

4-WHEEL-DRIVE JEEPS AND OTHER BIG UGLY BOXES

In Marion, South Carolina (pop. 10,000), where I have lived the past 12 years, the typical upscale young to middle-age white woman drives a Ford Explorer or similar sport utility vehicle (SUV). In recent years SUVs have become the rage here, especially among upper-middle-class, college-educated elites who are concerned about status.

I'm not really sure why this is. There are many things about contemporary North American culture that I fail to understand. Why, I wonder, would an attractive young woman want to ride around in a big ugly box? I'm told that some SUVs cost more than $30,000, too! I cannot imagine a sane person making payments on such a hideous-looking vehicle, but then, I've never ridden in one and have no idea what I'm missing. Probably not much.

The television commercials and magazine advertisements for SUVs lead you to believe they are extremely practical and indestructible, that you can go almost anywhere in them. After all, they have big, powerful gas-guzzling motors; they have fat, knobby tires; they sit high off the ground; and they have four-wheel drive. Still, I can't imagine any of these stylishly coiffed Southern belles driving to the Arctic Circle or down the Pan American Highway to Tierra del Fuego. Mostly they drive them to work, school and the shopping mall. And since it rarely ever snows here, I wonder why they need four-wheel drive.

I suspect the SUV craze has little to do with function and much to do with style and security. American culture has become increasingly obsessed with personal security and that in itself has become our style. Even though SUVs can easily roll over and are certainly more dangerous than conventional automobiles, there's an erroneous perception that to drive one is to be in control, to be prepared for whatever hazards — road or meteorological — may come our way.

So much of contemporary style seems, to me at least, to be in response to fear or insecurity. The advertisers warn us that it's a dangerous and uncivilized world out there; we need all the comfort and security we can get, regardless of the cost.

A television commercial now airing in South Carolina shows a smartly dressed middle-aged career woman (you can imagine her as an attorney or perhaps a financial consultant) and mother driving home from the office. Suddenly she's cruising past another young, attractive, stylishly dressed woman standing along the busy highway talking into a cellular phone. The second woman is obviously calling a wrecker because her car has broken down. The camera then zeroes in on the first woman's face as she approaches the stranded woman motorist. Fear, concern, anxiety — all are written across her face as she cruises by the woman talking into the cell phone. We, the viewers, are left to interpret her thoughts. I imagine her thinking, or perhaps even whispering, "Oh, thank heavens that's not me. I'm sure glad I'm driving this brand-new Buick LeSabre!"

The commercial is well-crafted. Woman No. 1 looks every bit the smug, white upper-middle-class, self-centered professional, who has deadlines to meet, clients to consult with, money to make. But in the next scene we see her warmer, softer side, as she picks up her young son at school. Ah, all is well. He happily climbs into that brand-new LeSabre and off they go toward the security of home. I imagine she is carrying her cellular phone. I also imagine she resides in an exclusive, "secure," perhaps gated community. And finally, before her little boy goes out to ride his bike, she will surely insist he strap on his plastic safety helmet.

The current trend in America is toward cultivating landscapes of fear. Why has it become so stylish for younger people to carry around those plastic water bottles? Has desertification overtaken the entire United States? Or have we Americans simply grown fearful of water fountains and faucets? Everything is now suspect. Germs are everywhere. Airport restrooms now dispense sanitary toilet seat covers. AIDS is rampant. You can't be too careful. Bottled water has become trendy.

The telephone rings. It's a telemarketer wanting to install a state-of-the-art security system in our home. We're not interested. We have a dog. She's our security system, along with our faith.

We are constantly bombarded with dire warnings: Dead-bolt your doors, check the batteries in your cell phone, check your blood pressure and cholesterol regularly, watch your weight, watch your salt and fat intake, don't smoke, get screened for breast, colon, and prostate cancer. Don't forget about the dangers of diabetes and herpes, too. The television news and talk shows are relentless in bombarding us with fear.

One of my friends recently chastised me for not having a will. I'm 46. We have no children. But he's right; we need to have a will drawn up. We probably need to be doing a lot of things we rarely ever think or worry about. I, especially, need to pay more attention to my spiritual health, never mind the physical. I recall my pastor warning, "You're only one breath away from seeing God."

We're also bombarded with warnings from financial planners who scare us about the future cost of a college education, of retirement, of having children, of dying. Even my favorite daily newspaper, *The Christian*

Science Monitor, has a regular Monday section now on "Work and Money." When the stock market plunged suddenly in late October, one of my friends asked me how my portfolio fared. "Portfolio? Uh, what exactly is that? No, I don't think I've got one."

We Americans are afraid of strangers, afraid of each other, afraid of our children, afraid of ourselves. We're afraid of going hungry, thirsty, getting fat, or going bald. We're afraid of middle age, old age, unemployment and retirement. We're afraid of darkness, sunlight, cities and wilderness. We're afraid of immigrants, rednecks, blacks, Indians and Arabs. We're afraid of failure. We're afraid to be different. We're afraid of life; we're afraid of death. We all seem to need psychoanalysis, yet we're afraid to get help because we're afraid it will show up on our employment record.

But fear sells. In a consumer society fear is a growth industry. Our culture has become obsessed with buying security. Even a college degree (not a college education) is now thought of by some parents and administrators (rarely by professors) as a form of financial security.

In reality, we Americans have much less to fear now than we did more than 50 years ago when F.D.R. warned, "The only thing we have to fear is fear itself." We're now living longer than at any other time in history. In 1900, the average U.S. life expectancy was 47; by the 1990s it was nearly 80. So I really wonder how badly we need our SUVs, car phones, home security systems, bottled water, bicycle helmets, stock portfolios, and annual medical screenings for countless diseases we don't have and probably will never get. If the disease runs in the family, that's another matter entirely. Heredity, our biological link to the past, is significant. But might we be happier and possibly even more secure if we gave up much of this other "security" and concentrated on things that mattered and were enduring?

But when something catches on in America — even something as ugly, expensive and inefficient as a gas-guzzling, road-hogging SUV — we gradually begin to see a curious beauty in it.

"Isn't that a pretty Explorer," I recently heard one of my friends remark.

"Boy, that's a beautiful pickup," another friend commented one day.

Pretty? Beautiful? I've heard such words used to describe quaint stone cottages with thatched roofs and window boxes brimming with flowers. But since when is a pickup truck or an SUV a thing of beauty? Have we no taste? Have we become so obsessed with buying security that we've become blind to the sheer ugliness it has all created?

Indeed, in our quest for personal and social security, we've turned our commercial landscapes into hideous strips of visual blight. Consider how the average American town has changed in the past 50 years: The downtowns have lost their retail function, to be replaced by finance companies, banks, and other lending and investment institutions. Nearby are the various clinics — medical, dental, chiropractic, psychological — devoted to healing our numerous physical and mental disorders. And then there's the commercial strip — hamburger alley — motels, mini-malls, automobile dealerships, cellular phone dealerships, mobile home sales, restaurants, retail outlets and very much more.

Consider the thousands of acres devoted to security-storage facilities alone. Think about how much farmland and timberland has been lost to parking lots, Wal-Marts, office parks, apartment complexes, shopping malls and supermarkets. Around the larger cities these strips now stretch for dozens of miles; they're called "edge cities."

And who wants to live amid this dehumanizing jumble of sprawling metal, plastic and concrete bunkers? Who indeed? This is why we long to escape in our pricey SUVs to "authentic" American landscapes — quaint small towns like Camden, Maine, or Gatlinburg, Tennessee, or perhaps, Estes Park, Colorado, where we can also "jump off" and have a real wilderness experience.

The highway (once it had been an Indian footpath) has become the most important cultural landscape in America. The road is a visual record of who we are. Millions of acres have been paved over to create multi-lane freeways, interchanges, bypasses, beltways, ramps, access roads, parking, service and retail facilities. Even in a rural state like Maine, one of the hottest political topics in recent years has been the proposed widening of the Maine Turnpike. But wouldn't this just be another step toward the destruction of the very "authenticity" that tourists drive thousands of miles in their big ugly boxes to see and experience?

Sometimes the interpretation of the American landscape is so clear-cut we fail to see the forest for the trees.

1997

17

ANTS

I knew there was something very wrong when we turned down the gravel road to our camp in Gouldsboro on June 3. It was the leaves: Even the poplars had sprouted leaves. Then I noticed that the apple blossoms had already gone by. For a second I wondered if we had gotten the date wrong. Was it the middle, rather than the beginning of June? I would soon discover that the lilacs had also peaked. I would be denied one of the simple pleasures I'd waited a whole year for: gathering Linda a big bouquet of purple and white lilacs from around an old cellar hole that most folks who use this road hardly know exists.

We'd been cheated out of at least two weeks of a Maine spring. But except for a couple of trees that were down, and several others that were leaning or had fallen in the heath behind our camp, everything looked OK. There were more dead flies than usual inside the camp, but nobody had bothered anything. I went up in the loft and noticed a few large black ants scurrying about.

"Linda, there's quite a few ants up here," I said. I opened the old pine trunk that I use as a seat for my writing desk and was not prepared for what I saw: ANTS! Hundreds, maybe thousands. They had laid scores of eggs, too. They had also eaten holes through the blankets inside. Our Army surplus mosquito net, which we had purchased in Salisbury, North Carolina, in 1981, was in ruins.

The pine trunk came out of the old Western Auto store in Harrington in 1973. I had a summer job just down the road, building a grass tennis court for an out-of-stater and happened to be on hand when the Western Auto store went out of business. I noticed that the proprietors were discarding some old junk. "Geez, do you suppose I could have that old pine box?"

"Sure, take her away," the man said. Back then I had practically no furniture in this camp. The pine box was missing a top, but I put a lid on it with hinges, and have used it for a seat and for storing blankets and clothing ever since.

I suspect the pine trunk has held up much better these past 25 years than the grass tennis court, because when we dug the post holes for the fence around it, the holes filled up with water. I remember saying to my friend Aidan, "They're wasting their money. We're on the floodplain here. Nature's going to destroy this thing in a few years."

Aidan said: "Who cares? It's a job. Plus, he gives us free beer." But

I said, "Don't you think we ought to tell them it's not going to last?" Aidan replied, "Look, the boss is an engineer, the owner's got plenty of money. What are you worried about?"

I had been studying geography and geology in college all year and was perhaps overly sensitive about environmental issues. I was also a naive, idealistic college student. Aidan was a young man — with a wife and two children to support. He was trying to survive in Downeast Maine.

I carried the pine trunk full of ants down from the loft, lugged it outside, sprayed the ants with Raid and aired it out for a couple of days. It's back where it belongs and I'm sitting on it as I write.

According to an Associated Press article, the warmer temperatures this winter have caused a surge in New England's carpenter ant population. Exterminators in New Hampshire are calling it "the year of the ant." Business for exterminators is booming as brand-new homes in that state and in nearby Massachusetts are already infested. Apparently the explosion of ants, like nearly every other natural disaster this year, is being blamed on El Niño.

Like everyone else in the Americas, I've been living with El Niño's wrath all winter and spring. I got four or five colds this winter and was the sickest I've been in years, probably from running every day in the chilly rain of South Carolina. I'd catch a cold, shake it, then have a relapse. It went on like that until the weather turned warmer in March.

Then I went to Mexico, where my eyes and lungs burned from clouds of dust blowing in the wind. I don't ever recall a dustier, windier March in Mexico. I also got to witness the beginnings of the fires that, by May, would destroy thousands of acres of Mexico's tropical forests.

El Niño is caused by a mysterious weakening of the southeast trade winds that blow counterclockwise across the southern hemisphere to make deserts of the west coasts of South America, Africa and Australia, since the winds are blowing down off the land rather than off the ocean. But when the southeast trades occasionally weaken, which usually becomes noticeable around Christmas, hence, the name El Niño — The Child — the cold water that typically flows northward up from Antarctica slows and washes back against Peru and northern Chile. The air above the Peruvian Current becomes unstable, and as it drifts back against the Andes Mountains, it rises, cools, and condenses into rain.

The Atacama Desert of southern Peru and northern Chile is the driest place on earth. But not during El Niño. Suddenly, places that haven't seen rain for years are deluged. Lima, Peru, is usually so dry that the shantytown dwellers on the city's outskirts do not even bother to put roofs on their shacks. El Niño spells disaster for them. They also like to build their outhouses over streams running down from the Andes so their waste can be carried out to sea. As long as the southeast trades blow strong and the Peruvian Current flows northwestward (counterclockwise) as usual, the waste from these sewers causes little harm. Enter El Niño, and you have sewage washing up on the beaches. Outbreaks of deadly cholera then follow.

As El Niño persists, the Pacific Ocean gradually warms up, triggering huge storms that move across North America driven by westerly winds. The more moisture in the atmosphere, the more it acts as an insulating blanket to keep temperatures warmer than normal. That results in ice storms in places such as Maine where there should be severe cold and snow. The warmer temperatures also bring an earlier spring with more blackflies, mosquitoes and ants.

But what is it that causes the southeast trades to weaken in the first place, triggering this whole El Niño sequence? I've been wondering about this since that summer in Harrington when I lay on my belly and reached down those post holes and bailed out the water so Aidan and I could build the fence around the ill-fated grass tennis court. I suppose the secret to the mystery of El Niño, along with most every other environmental problem on this planet, probably lies on that little estuary in Harrington. We better stop messing around with nature. The ants are trying to tell us something, and we had better pay attention.

1998

18

WYTOPITLOCK

Back in early June, when there was still the promise of a Maine summer, Linda and I drove to Wytopitlock. Nobody I knew in Gouldsboro had ever been there. Neither had we. We weren't even sure how to pronounce the name. Was it WHY-toe-pit-lock or Whit-to-pit-lock? Finally, one of my most learned friends, who also is a Maine native, said, "Hmm, yes, I believe that's Wita-pit-lock."

"Have you ever been there?" I asked.

"Uh. No. Don't know anybody who has."

"It's an Indian name, of course," explained the friendly woman who ran Crawford's Store in nearby Drew Plantation. There are no stores in Wytopitlock, which borders Drew Plantation.

"I have to drive to either Lincoln or Houlton to get my supplies," she continued. "They won't deliver down in here. I've got to drive more than 30 miles just to get milk and bread. It's a little isolated."

"How do you like it?" I wanted to know.

"Oh, I love it here. I'm originally from Old Town. My husband's from Wytopitlock."

"What do people in Wytopitlock do for a living?"

"Nearly everybody works in the woods. There's only about 30 that live here year-round."

Wytopitlock had a town hall, a church, another church that had fallen into ruin, a handful of modest houses, and a tiny village green with a war memorial. A lazy river meandered through the lush woods. It was not especially pretty, but it was pristine.

Two small boys stopped by the store on their bikes and bought candy. They didn't say much — a few grunts. They had those punk rocker haircuts with one side shaved and the rest of the hair growing wild. As far as I could tell, they were not aliens from another galaxy. A few minutes later, a young woman with a big, Paula Jones hairdo pulled up in a Pontiac Firebird and bought a pack of cigarettes. The place was jumping. The proprietor was all smiles.

Linda and I bought our own Wytopitlock-Drew Plantation T-shirts. The proprietor said, "I had a man in here all the way from New York City...He saw those shirts and said, "I've got to have some of those!" He was buying them for all his friends and relatives.

"There's some camps on the river," she continued. "A lot of them come for the hunting and fishing. The fishing's pretty good."

Just south of town we had stopped at an abandoned house that had been taken over by lilac and lupine. The lilac had gone by, but I jumped out of the car, and like a common thief, I picked Linda a big bouquet of lupine. I stood there a moment and listened. I could hear a lawnmower off in the distance. But little else. No cars. No voices. Just birds. Peace.

Perhaps one of the most comforting myths about Maine is that there is still a frontier; that if you've just had enough of the traffic, the trendiness, and the homogenization of the coast, you can always turn inland to the "real" Maine. There, in such pristine places as Enfield, Danforth, Howland, Macwahoc, Medway, Millinocket, Molunkus, Milo, Lee, Lincoln, Springfield, Waite, and Wytopitlock, you can still find "real" Maine people who haven't been ruined by the forces of American consumerism.

"I just got back from a Citgo convention in Nashville, Tennessee," the proprietor continued. "We stopped off in Dover, Delaware, for the stock car races. Had some awful thunderstorms when we was out in Tennessee. Tornado warnings. Wasn't it hot out there! I don't like that kind of weather. We was glad to get home."

I tried to imagine myself living in Wytopitlock. It was easy. It had everything I needed — a country store in nearby Drew Plantation, a river for bathing and fishing, plenty of deep woods, and no doubt, enough black flies, deer flies, horse flies and mosquitoes to keep most everyone else away. And if we sold our camp in Gouldsboro, we'd probably get enough cash to afford an even bigger piece of property in Wytopitlock, maybe even near the river! Oh, man! I can see it now! We could start building next summer. Ah! Such tranquility. Think of the writing I could do. Better yet, just think of the thinking I could do! No distractions... That does it for me. That's all I need. And my running: I could run for miles and miles. I wouldn't have to put up with traffic on Route 1 in Gouldsboro any longer.

It took us all day to get to and from Wytopitlock. We drove slowly, taking in the sights, and reveling in the beauty and splendor of the real Maine. But in the late afternoon, when we had finally gotten back down to around Ellsworth Falls, I suddenly said to Linda: "Oh! Oh! Oooh! Look! Look at that! The fog! Oh, look at all this fog! We didn't have any of that in Wytopitlock. You know, I'd really miss the fog."

"I know I would," Linda said.

By the time we got back to Gouldsboro, it was so damp in the camp we had to light the woodstove.

That night, as we stoked the fire and listened to the foghorns and the loons on the pond, I said to Linda, "You know, I'm not sure I'd ever be

happy living in Wytopitlock."
 Linda said, "I know I wouldn't."

   1998

19

THE NEW MAINE LANDSCAPE

A few years ago, when one of my high school classmates returned home to Maine after "hitting it big" on the West Coast, she and her husband bought some land on a secluded peninsula, then cut a mile-long driveway through the woods. I've never seen the house, but from all accounts its construction, along with the building of the roadway, were quite an undertaking, requiring considerable local expertise and costing, no doubt, a pretty penny.

In the old Maine landscape, people lived in villages, where their houses and their lives were in full public view. You simply knocked on the kitchen door, where you were warmly received and invited inside for conversation, a snack, or a cup of tea.

Occasionally, I bump into my former classmate's mother, who always asks me if I've seen her daughter since she moved back from the West Coast.

"No, I haven't," I always reply. And after 30 years, would I even recognize her?

Her mother always says, "I keep telling her to just pull you over when she sees you running along Route 1."

And I always say, "Yeah, I wish she would. Everybody else does."

That's an exaggeration, of course, but not entirely. I do take a long run each summer afternoon, up and down Route 1 from West Gouldsboro to East Sullivan and back, partly to see and visit with friends and former classmates. I'm frequently stopped out front of Young's Store by old friends in pickup trucks. I'm out there running every day, hoping to preserve my body and extend my life; but more importantly, I'm trying to save my soul. I need the contact. I need the daily interaction with my fellow human beings.

To be fair, I've often wondered what I'd have to talk about with this former classmate if I ever did meet her. She was a scholarship student who excelled in every way. Compared to me, she was a genius who could speak French fluently, recite Shakespeare flawlessly; she always had the leading role in school plays. She was also a cheerleader, and was, of course, very popular. Is it any wonder she hit it big and now holds down an important position over on "the island?" I, on the other hand, had graduated near the very bottom of my class. I was interested in hunting and fishing, motorcycles and sports. I was then, and still am, a rather "basic" creature.

Yet I, too, am a lover of privacy. Like a modern-day Thoreau, I'm still living...summers, with my wife, Linda, in a rustic cabin in the woods with no modern facilities. I'm still lugging firewood and water, and rowing around the pond in an old, leaky boat. But also like Thoreau, I'm very much the public man. Thoreau welcomed visitors at his humble cabin; he also spent a good deal of time out and about, on foot mostly, meeting and greeting friends and strangers along the way. He was a saunterer who needed human contact.

During the past couple of decades, thousands of private roads have been cut through the woods leading to once-secluded places along the Maine coast. The scarring of coastal land has been relentless. In Gouldsboro, the Knowles Company is currently putting in a subdivision on the Summer Harbor road for million-dollar homes. The entrance road is so wide and is such an egregious violation of nature...well...it just makes me ill.

Many of Downeast Maine's long driveways have signs that read "Private Road"; others are not posted — perhaps their owners feel that "Keep Out" signs are in bad taste, or else they do not want to anger the local clam or worm diggers. In any case, one is hesitant about driving down one of these private lanes without a proper invitation.

Last summer, when I had wanted to bring a book by a friend's home — another high school friend who had moved from an old house on the main road to a new place down a long, private lane — I first asked the advice of a mutual friend. "Uh, I'd like to take this book down to him because I think he'll enjoy it, but I just don't want to intrude on his privacy."

My friend said, "Go on down; he'll be glad to see you."

But then I reminded him that I do not have a telephone at camp and would be dropping in on him unexpectedly. "Oh, I think it would still be OK. Of course, you could call from here first."

I had once asked my friend what our mutual friend did for a living, as he didn't keep any special hours, had no specific commuting schedule. I knew only that he was his own man. My friend just said, "Oh, he's an investor."

"Of course," I said. I knew that he had a computer, because he had once e-mailed me in South Carolina about a particular author. He wondered if I had read him.

It took me three weeks to get up the nerve to drive down that lane. I chose a sparkling clear Saturday morning — about 9:30. I met his wife on the lane. He was shaving, she said, but he'd be delighted to see me. The visit went fine; we had a good chat, but I still wonder, should I have telephoned first, instead of just dropping in?

More than anything else, privacy has become the new American status symbol. Indeed, modern life, it seems, is an invasion of one's privacy. From the president on down, none of us wants to be caught with our pants unzipped, so we'll go to nearly any length and pay nearly any price to secure our privacy.

"People don't want you to know how much money they've got, or how they make it," another friend suggested. Certainly, just listening to the evening news, or even opening one's mail, you get the impression that privacy is rapidly vanishing. And then there are the relentless telemarketers who want you to let them into your house and into your life. You just want to say," Look, it's none of your damn business; just leave me alone."

But in a recent *New Yorker* essay, Jonathan Franzen suggests just the opposite; that modern Americans are "drowning in privacy."

> In 1890, an American typically lived in a small town under
> conditions of near-panoptical surveillance. Not only did his
> every purchase 'register' but it registered in the eyes and
> in the memory of shopkeepers who knew him, his parents,
> his wife, his children. He couldn't so much as walk to the
> post office without having his movements tracked and
> analyzed by neighbors. Probably he grew up sleeping in a
> bed with his siblings and possibly with his parents, too.
> Unless he was well-off, his transportation — a train, a horse,
> his own two feet — either was communal or exposed him to
> the public eye.

> In the suburbs and exurbs where the typical American lives
> today, tiny nuclear families inhabit enormous houses, in
> which each person has his or her own bedroom and sometimes,
> bathroom. Compared even with suburbs in the sixties and
> seventies, when I was growing up, the contemporary
> condominium development or gated community offers a
> striking degree of anonymity. It's no longer the rule that you
> know your neighbors. Communities increasingly tend to be
> virtual, the participants either faceless or firmly in control of
> the faces they present. Transportation is largely private; the
> latest S.U.V.s are the size of living rooms and come with
> onboard telephones, CD players, and TV screens; behind the
> tinted windows of one of these high-riding, I-see-you-but-you-
> can't-see-me mobile PrivacyGuard units, a person can be
> wearing pajamas or a licorice bikini, for all anybody knows or

cares. Maybe the government intrudes on the family a little more than it did a hundred years ago (social workers look in on the old and the poor, health officials require inoculations, the police inquire about spousal battery), but from a privacy perspective these intrusions don't begin to make up for the small-town snooping they've replaced.

Last summer, when my sister who lives in New York City came to visit us at our camp in Gouldsboro for the first time in 25 years, she suddenly looked through the woods toward a nearby camp and said: "Oh! I didn't realize you had neighbors! Do you know them, Al?" I was taken aback. Do I know them? I've known all of the people on our camp road for nearly three decades. We're like a family. I'm comfortable knocking on any of their doors at nearly any time of day or night. There was a time when nobody on this dirt road had electricity or telephones, and I guess we've never really gotten out of the habit of just dropping in unannounced. Thank heavens! Friends and neighbors drop by our camp all the time. It's nice. That's the old Maine landscape. I like it a whole lot better than the new one.

1998

20

RUNNING IN ULSTER

Ireland is green...even on March 4. But what impressed me even more than the lush, verdant landscape, were the daffodils. They were everywhere, big and bright and yellow, glorious row after row, and in some places, entire fields of them.

Linda and I went to Northern Ireland to a town called Armagh, not far southwest of Belfast. It's a religious place, with two St. Patrick's cathedrals — one Catholic, the other Protestant — both perched on high hilltops with breathtaking views of the surrounding rural landscape. To reach the Catholic St. Patrick's, you have to climb several flights of steep stone steps. And then, when you arrive breathless at the pinnacle, you can gaze downward upon the sinuous maze of narrow streets and densely packed dwellings in this medieval town, surrounded by miles of hilly green fields.

It was hard for me to believe I was really here (I had to pinch myself!), in Northern Ireland, looking out into a countryside that had seen more than its share of human drama, some of it violent and tragic. Many of those green fields held cattle, horses and of course, sheep. And the sheep — fat and fluffy with layers and layers of thick wool — were herded by black and white Border Collies, like out of a storybook, or perhaps the movie *Babe*.

Linda's grandfather had fled Armagh to America many years ago. There's a story there, no doubt, but no one seems to have the details. We tried in vain to find the name McNulty in the old graveyard adjacent to the cathedral. We padded back and forth over the soft grass-covered earth, examining the names on the gravestones. The harsh winter wind bit into our faces, as it had for many years weathered the headstones, until many of them had been rubbed almost bare. There could have been a slew of McNultys in that cemetery, but the names were all gone now.

But we weren't genealogists on a mission; rather, we were simply visitors, wondering what impression the Northern Irish landscape and its people would make on us. Would we want to return? Or would we conclude what others had concluded: that this was a drab and dangerous place — a poor second cousin to the real Ireland to the south?

I have to admit, I'm attracted to places that people are willing to shed blood over. The sight of policemen in bulletproof vests only heightened my interest; it made the landscape that much more appealing. This is my kind of place, I thought. I love Mexico for its passion, its poverty, its extreme wealth and its violence. Maybe I could get to love this tortured land, too?

At a bus stop in Newry, another town associated with violence and death, boys and girls in crisply pressed school uniforms — jackets and school ties, the girls in short skirts — laughed and joked while wet snow flurries rained down upon us in a strong northwest wind. It felt harsh to Linda and me, meaner than any wind we had endured during the mild South Carolina winter, but it didn't faze these youngsters. At last, the bus arrived and we climbed aboard, happy to have cover from the Irish winter. We hadn't cleared the outskirts of Newry before a drunken old man got on board and collapsed into the seat in front of us.

"Do you realize who I am?" he asked, as he turned around and grabbed my hand. "I haven't a clue," I said in an unwilling tone of voice, wishing he'd let go of my hand. He babbled on like a drunken idiot. He was a pest, a real nuisance. I wanted to smash him in the face. I was that tired, that irritable. After all, we'd had little sleep on the long flight and had been traveling for nearly 20 hours. But I was a stranger in this culture: I kept my composure, and it wasn't much farther before he suddenly let go of my hand, got up, and nearly fell out the door of the bus.

The young female driver must have known his routine. She hadn't charged him. We watched him weave a zig-zagging course across a field toward an apartment complex on a hill. The teen-age girls on the bus all laughed at him. I got the impression from the roadside litter around Armagh and Newry that alcohol abuse is at least as much of a problem here as it is in rural South Carolina, where the roadsides are peppered with empty liquor containers. I also got the impression that teenage girls grow up fast in Northern Island, the way they sometimes do in rural backwaters like Downeast Maine.

Meanwhile, the Ulster bus wound its way down narrow country lanes. The scenery was breathtaking. At one point, we abruptly stopped. The 20-something bus driver was lost (was this her first day on the job?) as she suddenly threw the bus into reverse, grinding the gears viciously while the boys in the back seats just howled. At that moment, we looked out the bus window and saw two beautiful black and white Border Collies. They sat ever so calmly and regally at the edge of the road. Oh, how I wanted to pet a dog! I was missing Bessie, our own Border Collie, something awful. Travel — it can be wonderful and miserable at the same time!

"This is a wonderful place!" I said to the desk clerk our first evening at the Charlemont Arms Hotel, where we stayed in Armagh. "I think we're going to stay over the weekend."

She looked at me like I was out of my mind. Perhaps I was. But I was also sincere. I couldn't have been more pleased with the hotel, the town, the people, or the setting. There was something absolutely wonderful about this place that I couldn't quite put my finger on. There was a warmth among the people here that I hadn't anticipated. And that warmth was extended to us. Folks went out of their way to be helpful and courteous. Nevertheless, about a week after we returned from Northern Ireland, a woman was blown up in a car bombing not far from here. She was a lawyer who had defended several people in Portadown, another town we visited.

The sun would appear for just a few minutes; then it felt warm...well, sort of. Most of the time it was overcast with a stiff northwest wind blowing. I marveled at how it could feel so cold, yet appear so green and springlike. But it never got much below freezing at night, and then it didn't remain cold for long.

Ireland is continually bathed by the warm waters of the North Atlantic Current, which moderates the temperature, allowing palm trees to grow in the British Isles at latitudes comparable to Hudson Bay in North America.

Irish women have beautiful complexions. We all know the sun is bad for our skin. I was also moved by the softness of the Irish women's eyes and voices...Is it any wonder I married a woman who is part Irish? It's a great climate for sheep and Border Collies and, of course, long-distance running.

I had always wanted to run in Ireland. And that, perhaps more than any other, was the reason I had come. So despite my jet lag and a cold rain that seemed to come in waves, I took off running through the streets of Armagh, all the way out a narrow road called Munnerlin Lane, into the Irish countryside. Now I was in Ireland! All alone in a cold pelting downpour, galloping past fields where large farm horses wrapped in warm woolen blankets stood silently watching, my run became a celebration of my arrival — for having lived long enough to finally get here, for being the only person in my family or Linda's to experience this place and moment in such a way...to be able to run down this glorious road! Hedgerows of rose bushes lined the way. How beautiful they would be in a few months! But this was just fine. I was soaked to the bone, but warm inside.

I had run a marathon in Myrtle Beach, South Carolina, just three days before. My legs were still throbbing. My knees ached from the dampness. I'm nearly 48. It was my 52nd marathon, and I really felt my middle age. Still, Ireland made me want to run another marathon. The magic of the place inspired me; it made me want to run faster. The walls of Irish pubs are often lined with pictures of great Irish runners. Distance running is celebrated in Ireland, as it should be. I couldn't imagine coming here and not having the urge to run like a Celtic harrier.

Ireland didn't interest me as much as move me with its warmth and its charm. Mexico is, to me, a much more interesting country. But I didn't come to Ireland as a scholar; I came, simply, to see if the place would stir me. It did. In a very short time the island grew on me. And except for the currency change, you hardly realized any difference between north and south. The people are, as they say, "luvly" in each place. The landscape doesn't change (it's beautiful in Northern Ireland and in the Irish Republic), only the politics, but those "troubles" finally seem to be mending.

We made no advance hotel reservations. We just showed up at the airport. I didn't even want to look in a guidebook; rather, I purposely went to Ireland as blind as a bat just to "see" if the place would move me. I found myself looking hard at people's faces, listening to their accents and their talk, examining their houses, towns and neighborhoods.

My curiosity grew with exposure. It wasn't there naturally, like it has always been with Mexico and other areas of the Third World. I would just as soon have stayed in South Carolina than to fly more than eight hours on an airplane to any place in Europe. Always a most reluctant traveler, I had to force myself to go to the airport. I had dreaded the trip so much that I tried not to even think about it until the day we left. But all that has changed.

Coming home, we flew right over the state of Maine. I looked down from 35,000 feet at the snow and ice-covered landscape. I looked in vain for our tiny camp in Gouldsboro, realizing that we'd be there in a few short months. But I was also coming to another realization: We were no longer at the end of our Ireland journey, but only the beginning. This Irish business is going to cost me some money. We were already making plans to return next spring.

1999

21

RABBIT SALAD SANDWICHES

When I was a boy, back in the early 1960s, my favorite television shows were *Combat* and *The Gallant Men*. Both were about combat soldiers in the European theater during the Second World War. I believe The *Gallant Men* was set in Italy, and *Combat*, starring Vic Morrow, one of my boyhood heroes, was supposed to take place in France.

Vic Morrow played an army sergeant. He was a tough guy who hated the war. I was especially fascinated by his weapon, a small submachine gun of some sort. I used to know the names and models of all the small-caliber weapons used in World War II, but that knowledge seems to have left me. *Combat* episodes always ended with firefights, and Vic Morrow, even though his comrades were often hit, or pinned down under heavy Nazi fire, always managed to prevail. In the end, he'd cut down every last one of "those lousy Krauts," as they were called back then.

I carried a gun around with me nearly everywhere I went in the early 60s, an air rifle that made a "pop," resembling a real weapon. I worshipped guns. I couldn't imagine my life without them. I was always drawing pictures of guns in school. I couldn't wait until I'd be old enough to have a real gun. I loved anything military. I had old World War I and World War II helmets, canteens, ammunition belts, even a gas mask. My father and I used to rummage around the Goodwill and the Salvation Army in Newark, New Jersey. That was where I bought most of my old army surplus stuff.

I used to wear a jacket around the neighborhood with corporal stripes and other badges and emblems sewn on the sleeves. My dream back then was to grow up to be a combat soldier. "I love war," I always used to say. "I sure hope there'll always be wars." Could I have been so prescient?

Growing up, I remember watching dozens of old World War II movies made in the 1940s and 1950s; and of course, I couldn't get enough of John Wayne, my favorite Hollywood actor. Even a decade or so later, when I was in my late teens and early 20s — during the Vietnam War when guys like John Wayne were no longer considered "cool" — I still enjoyed his films. He never did go out of style with me. I still enjoy watching his later Westerns, when he was an old man — 1970s movies like *Big Jake* and *The Cowboys*. In *The Cowboys*, he gets shot several times, but he keeps on fighting 'til the end. As a child, I always admired those men who kept on fighting despite terrible odds; who somehow kept moving forward in a hail of bullets, despite being hit several times, and no doubt, close to death. I was certain that life was about looking death in the eye, taking tremendous risks, and, despite terrible odds, prevailing in the end.

I had an excellent history teacher in the seventh grade who was an expert on World War I. I loved the stories he told our class about trench warfare, especially about when the first Americans were sent over to France. I remember him saying, "And word soon got around the trenches that the Yanks could fight." He'd whisper it to the class, as if he were a German solider in the trenches — "The Yanks can fight! The Yanks can fight!" My head swelled with pride. I'll never forget this man. I hung on his every word. He was a great classroom teacher and storyteller. He'd make us go to the library and do research on the mobilization in 1914 and on various other aspects of the war. He'd read us passages from *All Quiet on the Western Front*. I loved World War I. I'd have given anything to be in one of those trenches. I'd come home from school, grab my air rifle, and put on my gas mask.

My father died suddenly in 1966. We moved that summer from suburban New Jersey to rural Washington County, Maine. I was 15 then, and a year later when I turned 16, I finally got to have a real gun. By my senior year of high school I owned four guns — a 16-gauge shotgun, a bolt-action .22-caliber rifle with a seven-shot clip, a 6.5-millimeter Japanese rifle, and my favorite gun, a .303-caliber British Enfield.

During the winter of 1968-69, I killed 16 snowshoe hares, many of them with the British Enfield. I used steel-jacketed military ammunition that made a clean hole through the big rabbits. I skinned, cleaned and consumed them all. My mother grew up in the Depression; she's never believed in wasting food. She cooked the tough, gamey meat, chopped it up real fine, then added celery and mayonnaise to make rabbit salad sandwiches for my school lunches. She did the same with the ducks and grouse I shot. Some of my classmates thought I was a little weird, but many of them were also hunters. In fact, a lot of my classmates carried their .22-caliber rifles with them on the school bus when we had hunter-safety classes. Hunting was then, and still is, an important part of the culture in Maine.

I never succeeded in bagging a deer. I guess because I never acquired the know-how. My father had never hunted, so I had to learn about real guns and hunting from my friends. My father was a city boy, raised in Newark and Philadelphia; I don't think he ever fired a gun in his life. He missed out on the Second World War because of his high blood pressure. I suspect he would have been one of those voters who endorsed gun control legislation. I'm in favor of some gun-control measures myself. I'm especially bothered by the proliferation of assault rifles.

There are a lot of things that bother me about contemporary American culture. Nothing rankles me more, however, than our growing aversion to risk — in particular, our obsession with putting protective padding over every joint on our children's bodies, and keeping everything sharp or dangerous, such as knives or guns, out of their hands. Maybe it's because we're having so few children now, but for some reason, Americans have lately become obsessed with trying to protect their children from every conceivable danger, no matter how big or small. In the process, we may actually be harming many of our children, especially boys, who are in turn, flailing away at society for reasons neither they nor we can explain.

What most children need more than anything is adventure, challenges (especially physical challenges), and a certain amount of danger and risk taking. What they do not need is more middle-class suburban security. (Some children can't even ride their bikes around the block anymore without their neurotic parents strapping those plastic helmets on their heads!) Why not encourage these kids, especially the boys, to hunt, fish, swim, and sail; but even more importantly, to learn to explore on their own? This is how character, confidence, self-esteem, and especially, judgment is acquired. Children's lives are increasingly scheduled and programmed, cutting into precious free time, stifling natural curiosity and creativity. Why do children need all these organized activities?

Can't we trust them with free time? Why not let the boys, especially, seek out adventure? Even in urban and suburban areas, boys can explore old railroad and power line right-of-ways, riverbanks, back streets and alleyways, vacant lots, landfills and city dumps. What's wrong with allowing a 12-year-old boy to have a pellet gun so he can hang out at the landfill with his buddies, plinking at rats?

The important thing is that they spend time exploring the outdoors; on the lakes, streams, bays, and rivers; in the automobile graveyards and landfills; in the woods, gravel pits and abandoned strip mines; rather than at the mall, the video arcade, or in their bedrooms in front of computer screens. Children need to be exposed gradually to the real world; they should not be allowed to waste away in a virtual world.

Boys are hunters; girls are domesticators and nurturers — so the anthropologists tell us. Perhaps we should be listening to the anthropologists, rather than the politicians, psychologists and talk-show celebrities. How many of those folks have ever hunted rabbits, skinned and cleaned the meat, bitten through the sinew? I'm inclined to believe that hunting, fishing and outdoor life (whether urban or rural) are good for certain kids — especially boys like me who never quite fitted in — that over time, hunting and fishing teach you to respect life, not destroy it.

My years in the woods taught me how ecosystems work. I became a lover of plants and animals. My years of exploring cities and suburbs helped me vanquish my prejudices and appreciate cultural diversity. Fortunately, I had been given the freedom as a child, and as an adolescent, to roam and explore on my own; to hunt, fish, and swim; to take some risks and experience some dangers; to build self-confidence and self-esteem. Over time, those freedoms transformed me from a naive, somewhat aggressive child, to a gentler, more mature and thoughtful adult.

I haven't hunted in nearly 30 years. Sometime around age 20 or 21, I sold all of my guns, including my beloved British Enfield. I still like to fish, hike, run, swim, row a boat and explore, but I'm no longer interested in killing any game. I'm content to leave that to others. Our home here in South Carolina — a gun-toting state — has no firearms, no security system. All we have for protection is our faith, our common sense, our judgment, and a 36-pound Border Collie who sleeps under our bed at night.

Perhaps it was simply adolescent testosterone that made me love guns and rabbit hunting and movies about the horrors of war. I suspect it had at least as much to do with evolutionary biology as it did with culture. All that mayhem and killing simply appeals to some adolescent boys; it occasionally appeals to middle-aged men.

A good friend, who recently turned 50, and who saw plenty of action in Vietnam, freely admits to liking movies with "a lot of fightin' and killin' in 'em." Not me. Not any more. I haven't even seen *Saving Private Ryan*. Just reading the reviews convinced me it was far too graphic for my sensibilities. I don't have the stomach for that sort of mayhem anymore. I got it all out of my system hunting rabbits in the Maine woods.

1999

22

THIRTY YEARS LATER — A FAILED ATTEMPT AT UNDER-STANDING STEUBEN'S ELUSIVE GEOGRAPHY

The House in the Village

In August of 1969, when I first went away to college, my mother and I lived in an 1830s Cape Cod house on Old Route 1 in Steuben Village. The house is still there; I walked all around it in June of 1999 — trespassing, I'm afraid — just to see how it felt to set foot on my old turf. It seemed perfectly normal, as though I had never left. The current owners are from out-of-state. Nobody was at home when I tiptoed around the premises that sunny June morning. I would have asked permission had I seen anyone about. I might even have summoned the courage to knock on the door and introduce myself as the boy who once lived there. But the driveway was empty; the lawn needed mowing. I didn't see any harm in taking a quick look around. The place looked derelict; it needed a new roof and no telling what else. The house needed a lot of work back in 1969. The big silver maple tree that stood beside the driveway is gone now, but the crab apple on the west side of the house is flourishing. I can still remember how it smelled in late summer when it was laden with fruit.

I loved Steuben. I still do. I have this fantasy of returning some day and living out my life there. My parents bought that old farmhouse in 1959. It lacked indoor plumbing, but they hired a local man to install a regular bathroom in a tiny second-story closet of a room, underneath the eaves of the steep, gabled roof. For some reason, the local man, who was himself rather tall, decided to place the toilet very close to the outside wall. This made it awfully hard to use, especially if you were over four feet tall! It was extremely awkward for my father, who was a big man, over six feet.

We used to come up from New Jersey each summer and spend my father's precious two or three weeks vacation in the house. But on the last night of our vacation in July of 1966, my father had a massive heart attack. My mother said he died in the ambulance on the way to the hospital in Ellsworth. My mother sold our home in New Jersey that summer, and we moved up to the house in Steuben. She eventually hired two local carpenters to bump up part of the roof, so we could at last use the toilet without banging our heads.

I had lived in the same house in New Jersey the first 15 years of my life, so the move to Maine that summer, and the transition to Sumner

Memorial High School, were difficult. I was introverted and shy; and worse, I had never played basketball — it meant nothing in central New Jersey where high school wrestling was the big winter sport — so it took me a long time to make friends. I'm not sure I would have survived that first year at Sumner had it not been for the warmth and kindness of the people of Steuben. They graciously accepted my mother and me; they helped us out when in need; they especially made me feel, in a very short time, at home there. I quickly grew to embrace Steuben, so much so, that it has always given me pain that I went away at all. Never leave a place that you love; it will gnaw at your soul 'til the very end. I have often wondered what my life would have been like had I stayed right there all these years like most of my classmates and found a way to make a living in the local economy.

So this summer, 30 years later, I decided to return to Steuben to see what had changed. It was to be a sort of homecoming celebration. I recently turned 48, the age my father had been when he died in 1966. And it seemed fitting that I return to the very setting that had once given me so much pain and sorrow; only later, to bring me such joy and happiness. My high school years became a time of healing. I made friends. I adjusted to life without my father. I grew up. By the time I left Steuben in 1969, I was convinced that many of the best things in life come out of the worst tragedies.

A Plan of Study

Steuben has an immense, sprawling geography, with three large bays and several villages or hamlets, each with a slightly different look and character than the others. It is indeed a fascinating place that is worthy of years of study. The town of Steuben has more than 1,000 inhabitants, and includes villages such as Dyers Bay, Pigeon Hill, East Steuben, Steuben Village, Number Seven, Smithville, and Unionville. But there are also several other hamlets such as Dolly Head, Goods Point, Morse District, Petit Manan Point, and Wilderness Shores.

My plan was to drive over to Steuben each day, park my car, and eventually walk all the town roads; and in some areas, the shorelines as well. It was an ambitious goal, far too rigorous to complete in a summer. I must have thought I was invincible; I had outlived my father. I was hiking every morning, then running my usual eight to ten miles every afternoon. But in mid-July, during a failed attempt to walk all the way around Petit Manan Point, I twisted my knee on a beach of rounded stones. Then I tripped and fell on my run that afternoon. I felt a sharp pain below the kneecap. But I kept running and hiking, and it wasn't long before I wound up at the Gouldsboro Medical Clinic. The knee was inflamed. I couldn't walk. I had to hop around on one foot. It made it impossible to complete the project, so I'm calling it "a work in progress." Meanwhile, the knee is still giving me trouble.

I'm a cultural geographer, not a journalist. I didn't set out to interview people; rather, I wanted to walk slowly, examining the visual landscape, all the time reflecting on it, and trying to make sense out of what I saw. Of course, whenever I encountered townspeople I was delighted to talk to them. But formal interviews, I decided, would have to come later, after I had done some field exploration, after I had seen the landscape close-up and had raised some valid questions, and perhaps drawn some conclusions — right or wrong — about what I thought I was seeing. Then maybe I could begin a more systematic study of each of Steuben's hamlets and write it up as a story, or a geography of a Maine coastal town at the Millennium.

I was a little uneasy too, about where I wanted to walk. We Americans often exercise or stroll along city or suburban streets, but we seldom walk the bays and roads in rural areas, especially with a camera ready, and at a slow enough pace to really comprehend and record what we see. Such "rambling" through the countryside, as it is known in Britain, is uncommon in America. The distances here are vast, the motor vehicles are often traveling at high speeds, the roadways are dangerous. Residents of rural areas are likely to view such walkers with suspicion. Indeed! Who is that foolish tourist walking the roads with a camera? Hasn't he got anything better to do? He must be numb'er than a hake.

That could be. Because...as I began my research, I soon found that much of Steuben is now off-limits. It's a loose collection of tiny closed societies. I was trying hard to "see" the whole place, but I was constantly bumping up against NO TRESPASSING signs. In a few areas, when my curiosity simply got the better of me, I ignored the signs and ventured down the roads anyway. Not a good idea! Not only was I trespassing, but I was becoming increasingly depressed, as I realized that the biggest change in the town these past 30 years is the sheer amount of land, especially along the coastline, that is now posted.

So I found myself sticking to town roads, or else hiking around the shoreline, which, I understand is still public space. Americans nowadays tend to walk on hiking paths like the Appalachian Trail, or along designated "nature trails," but rarely do we saunter past the widely-spaced dwellings of the rural landscape. And that's exactly what I wanted to do. What can you learn from a nature trail other than about nature itself? As much as I love the natural world, I'm human, and what I really wanted to know was: Who lives in those rural houses, trailers, and double-wides? How do they make a living? What are their lives like? Indeed, it is the built landscape, or the absence of it, that tells us about our culture. The chained and unchained dogs of various breeds and temperaments; the lawn ornaments, gas grills, plastic toys and furniture, boats, all-terrain vehicles; the gardens and shrubbery; and of course, the size and style of the houses and outbuildings — all reveal much about the inhabitants of the place, about their ages, interests, values, and livelihoods.

Observations and Encounters

I began my walks at Whitten Parritt Stream, at the western edge of Steuben. I bought a fishing license. I went trout fishing. And there amongst the alders, balsam, spruce, and weeds surrounding a small pool, I found a discarded half-pint plastic container that read: "Take a Kid Fishing Today." Then, "15 Crawlers for $2.29." Don't kids dig their own angleworms anymore? It was the fourth day of a warm, and what would turn out to be, an extremely dry June. I didn't like it; I felt cheated out of a normal Maine spring. The water was low, and warmer than usual. I didn't expect to catch anything. I caught three brook trout — seven, eight, and nine inches.

"I'm not surprised," a friend said. "Geez, nobody around here goes fishin' anymore. None of the kids go." But I also found, in those bushes by the stream, a heavy-duty plastic ziplock bag containing 15-pound-test line, hooks large enough to land a codfish, a jar of Salmon Eggs, and a one-blade jackknife. Somebody around here went fishing. "They don't know how to fish," my friend continued. "Nobody's taught them how."

And where were these children? I know the birthrate has fallen in Maine, but the Ella Lewis Grammar School is still open. Yet in all of my summer walks around the bays, I never encountered a single child! We kids used to hang-out down at the town wharf. That's where we used to go swimming when the tide was high. At low tide, we swam in a pool on Tunk Stream called the Eel Pond. Another friend, who has teenaged children, told me he was putting in a swimming pool behind his home. I don't suppose anyone swims in the Eel Pond anymore, but I did discover some discarded clothing on the rocks further upstream at a place we kids used to call Dizzy Rock.

Occasionally, I'd see children at Mathews Country Store. Once, when I was Pumping gas, two boys on bicycles noticed my South Carolina license plate. One of the boys then said, "You ever been to North

Carolina?" "Yep." "You ever go to a basketball game there?" "Oh, yeah." "Cool! Awesome!" Then they peddled away, down Route 1. They were the exception. I didn't encounter any other kids on bikes during my many walks through the village.

Nationwide, it is estimated that less than one percent of children ages 7 to 15 ride bikes to school, a whopping 65 percent decline since the 1970s. Bicycle sales have been flat for years. Why? Some of the reasons often cited are an absence of sidewalks, parental fears of crime and traffic, tight scheduling of organized activities, television, and computer time. Many kids today would rather play a computer or video game than ride a bike. Indeed, some of the kids I observed at Mathews Country Store were quite "large." They hardly looked fit enough to ride a four-wheeler, let alone peddle a bicycle. Steuben's children may be typical of American kids at the end of the century.

According to John Stilgoe (1994, p. 386), a professor of landscape history at Harvard University, a new type of child has come along in recent years who has completely lost touch with the outside world, especially the coastal realm.

> An eight-year old boy sits aloof on the sandy beach one
> headland north of the secret one, whines he is "sea-sick,"
> nauseated by the smell of sea and seaweed, worried that
> people pee in the ocean, and disturbed by the dirtiness, the
> darkness of the sea, so unlike a clean swimming pool. The
> historian overhears, and stops thinking about dune preservation
> in the 1920s. Who is this boy? What is he?

This may partly explain why I did not encounter a single small boat on my walks around the inner part of Steuben Bay. The clammers don't even bother with skiffs anymore; they use four-wheelers to get down to the flats. The only small boats I found were rotting and abandoned. When I was a teenager, we had wooden boats that we used for dubbing around. I remember buying an old skiff from a fellow in Gouldsboro for just six dollars. Later, I built a new one in woodshop at Sumner High. The bay and the two streams, Tunk and Whitten Parritt, were the major playgrounds for us boys in the village.

I wonder, do kids here still grow up understanding the natural world? How fortunate they are to have such a fabulous marine laboratory less than half a mile from Ella Lewis Grammar School. Forget the Internet; the bay is much better; it's also a real place. When we first moved here from New Jersey in 1966, it was a local boy who taught me how to eat raw goosegrass, dig clams and bloodworms; and in December, to go frost-fishing for Tomcod. Another friend taught me how to hunt grouse and rabbits and deer, net smelts in the spring, and catch eels in Tunk Stream as big around as a man's fist. Do local children still explore the bays and brooks, or are the outdoors appreciated more nowadays by out-of-staters who come here with their kayaks and build their waterfront homes and revel in the extraordinary beauty? Stilgoe (1994, p. 387) says bluntly that:

> Kids are fat. Obesity is more than a national problem, it is now a national scandal, something Europeans notice immediately, especially at beaches. By any standard from the 1960s schoolroom charts to modern insurance-company tables to contemporary fashion articles, Americans are flabby, and many are so ashamed of how they look in a swimsuit that they choose not to visit beaches at all. But nowadays any honest observer at most beaches notices what medical researchers have so precisely documented. Kids are fat. At the beach, shorn of their stylish baggy pants, one-size-fits-all sweatshirts, and flapping overblouses, kids display jiggling, bouncing rolls of fat.

Although I did not encounter any children on my many walks around Steuben Bay, I did discover four new houses in the mile-long stretch between Mainayer Campground on Whitten Parritt Stream and the town wharf at the estuary of Tunk Stream. Four new houses were built in the past 30 years. Not bad. It is comforting to realize that not all of the Maine coast has been subdivided and violated. Two of the houses were built recently; one was so new the lawn had just been seeded, and the new occupants had not yet arrived. It was an impressive, architect-designed structure — a large, modern version of a traditional Cape Cod, with a second-story deck facing westward towards the Gouldsboro shore. The house stands on a bluff at the end of Baker's Point. It is positioned at a slight diagonal so the front faces eastward across the bay towards the Rogers Point Road. Morning light, setting sun, acres of mudflat at low tide; but oh, what a stupendous view — all the way out to Lobster Island — the occupants will have at high tide! I've always thought the bay was prettiest in winter with the low-angle sun glinting off the snow and ice. A large detached garage in the saltbox style stands behind the house. It's all in good taste. The exterior wood siding will weather, and blend in beautifully with its surroundings.

Still, it saddened me to discover this once pristine shoreline subdivided and developed. The gravel road into the subdivision passes through a wet, balsam forest — a dreary, brooding woods best left alone. A couple of good (normal) wet years and the bog will reassert itself; the road will need constant maintenance. I hunted snowshoe hares and partridges in those boggy woods 30 years ago. Not anymore.

Leaving Baker's Point, and walking down Old Route 1 towards Steuben Village, I stopped and visited a man I knew back in the 1960s. He's lived all these years in a derelict old 19th century farmhouse. (Such a contrast from the modernity I had just witnessed!) He's now 78. He has no telephone, no working television, no water in his well that is fit to drink. He apologized for his full beard and said, "I don't have any water. I'm saving my pennies to get one of those artesian wells. But they're very expensive." I asked him how he managed without water. He held up a half-gallon jug of water and said, "I buy a couple of these whenever I get to the grocery store. The minister over here drives me to Ellsworth."

He had been an Air Force pilot. And in World War II, he had flown DC-3's on some of the most dangerous missions of the Pacific Theater — over the "Hump," over the eastern ranges of the Himalayas, from Burma into China. "The mountains right there were over 14,000 feet," he explained. "I remember lookin' at the service manual and reading that the DC-3 would only fly as high as 17,000 feet."

We sat outside his home in the shade of a gnarly old apple tree. He had a little flower garden started in a circle around its base. He'd left the seed packets with the names of the various flower varieties in the foreground. I remarked that the seeds seemed to be coming along nicely in spite of the dry summer. He smiled and nodded in agreement. He was trying to get a small cooking fire started with a few twigs and a half-dozen charcoal briquettes. "I'd offer you a hotdog, but I've only got this one here," he apologized. "Maybe I'll be able to at least offer you a hotdog the next time you come by."

He got around with great difficulty, with the aid of a steel cane. It looked home-made. He was nearly blind. His wife had died of cancer more than 20 years earlier; and his only child, a daughter, had not been home for a visit in nearly two years. When I had first introduced myself, I had asked him how he'd been getting along. "Oh, I can't complain," he said with a warm smile and not a trace of bitterness. "Life's a little slow. But I've always liked things quiet...so I guess I'm doing alright."

He was a forgotten hero...in the greatest conflict of the 20th century. I couldn't even imagine the history he'd been part of, the things he had seen, the world he had known. He'd been all over Asia during the war; he'd flown across the Pacific numerous times. His grace and demeanor, even his manner of speech, were quaintly reminiscent of Hollywood actors in old 1940s movies. "Please tell your mother I was asking about her," he said, as I headed down the road. His was my father's and mother's generation — raised during the Great Depression, frugal, independent, hardworking, and thoughtful; revelling in all of life's glories, yet taking nothing for granted.

The East Side Road

Although new houses have been built by the thousands in southern Maine during the 1990s, I discovered four abandoned homesites — there may be others — on the East Side Road in Steuben. Three of these home-sites were actual cellar holes; the fourth was the charred skeleton of a much smaller dwelling, perhaps a camp. The cellar holes were small. Two of them measured 16 by 22 feet on the inside; the third was 22 by 28 feet, with a four by eight foot extension in the rear. These foundations were also shallow, usually four or five feet in depth, depending on the slope of the ground, but below the 36 inch frostline. Cellars, which would have required considerable backbreaking labor in the 19th century, were typically built under the main part of the house only. The kitchens, which were usually added on to the back and attached to connected barns, often lacked cellars. They were then banked with fir boughs, which collected the winter snow, and insulated the building. The foundation stones on the East Side Road were slabs of granite, irregular and crude. Old cellar holes such as these are not hard to find; you simply look for old apple trees, lilac bushes, phlox, roses, and other perennials. The foundations I discovered were interesting for their size and construction, but also for their contents: over the years they had become receptacles for discarded household waste.

The contents of the third, and largest, cellar hole were the most inter-esting and enlightening. The foundation stood about 50 feet back from the road. Balsam, birches, maples, and spruce grew from the inside, while out back was a magnificent cluster of ripe raspberries interspersed with a few young cherry and poplar trees. I remained there for several minutes, par-taking of the succulent berries and swatting at the myriad of deer flies, all the time marveling at the discarded treasures, which included an old bicy-cle frame, some rusty appliances, a hot water heater, old sofa springs and stuffing, aluminum cans, Clorox bottles, styrofoam, old shoes, plastic oil cans, tires, a kitchen range, mason jars, two plastic dishdrainers, a fiber-glass snowmobile body (an Alouette whose license had expired in June '74), plastic jugs, a coffee maker, folding lawn furniture, laundry deter-gent, sheetrock, beer bottles, Tropicana Orange Juice bottles, Mead Johnson-Enfamil Infant formula, children's boots, chainsaw oil, dish detergent, a chrome automobile bumper — all the detritus of a typical middle-class Downeast existence from the last half of the 20th century.

The last site was an old charred wooden frame, ten feet by fourteen. Inside was a rusted-out woodstove, a rusted-out gas refrigerator, and an old rusty Coca Cola cooler, while 30 feet or so back were the remains of an outhouse, a one-seater.

I wondered, of course, what treasures might be lining the bottom of these cellar holes. I hadn't the time, the inclination, nor the fly dope to find out. And...there I was, trespassing again...me, and my dog, Bess, sniffing through the garbage like a couple of hungry strays.

Who lived in those houses? What had their lives been like? Where had those people gone? "But you see, they burned. They all went into cellar." That was what Flossie Vasquez had told me in 1988. She was 98 then, still lived on her own, and still retained vivid memories of a community up there early in the century. "They raised apples. Those were their taxes," Flossie explained, meaning they made enough money from their apple crop to pay their property taxes.

No doubt, in that era of hand-dug wells, those places high up along the East Side Road would have been among the first in town to go dry. It was dry as dust this summer. I wondered how they could have survived such a year. The sphagnum moss crunched underfoot as early as June; by July, the woods were a tinderbox. It was easy to see how these houses could have burned, and perhaps easy to understand why others had not been built in their places. Despite all of our technological advances, there are still some environments unyielding to humanity's wishes.

The Jacob Townsley House, a large colonial structure dating from 1785, occupies a bluff northwest of the entrance to the East Side Road. The home is currently being restored by descendants of the Henry D. Moore family, for whom the Steuben Parish House is named. Flossie's little trailer-home stands empty a few hundred yards down the road on the left. Her bright orange Tiger Lilies and other perennials continued to bloom brilliantly this dry summer, as if she were still there tending them. Perhaps she is! Her warmth and brightness will wane slowly, if ever. Flossie blessed this community for 101 years.

It feels at least ten degrees hotter as you walk uphill into the mostly second-growth woods along the East Side Road. It's amazing how many microclimates there are in a coastal community like Steuben. The deer-flies on a hot summer day are absolutely wicked up here; they swirl around your head, pricking your neck and back in places you can't easily reach. And when you are lucky enough to nab one, it typically bursts, splashing your clothes with blood.

The East Side Road reaches its highest elevation about a mile beyond where the pavement ends. The top of the hill is a rocky, overgrown blue-berry field. Thirty years ago, the hill was still relatively free of brush. You could look down and see the church steeple on the village green;

which makes me think the field was still being harvested in the early 1960s. Now it's good cover for small game, such as the partridges Bess and I startled as we climbed the hill. Old logging tracks snake off in two directions: westward down to Tunk Stream; eastward, towards Milbridge and Cherryfield.

Continuing northward, the road begins a sharp descent, all the way down to Tunk Stream and into the hamlet of Smithville, where sawmills were located in the 19th century. The road grows wider as one descends, with much evidence of recent logging. The land scarification caused by heavy equipment is ugly and disheartening; it is the price paid for the efficiency gained from modern skidders. Looking backward to skipjacks, then even further back to horse-drawn sleds, you can tell by the width of the logging road and the depth of its ruts, the approximate age and type of equipment used. Many of the old logging roads are delightful, tree-covered tunnels of rare beauty; more recent roads are simply open wounds in the wilderness fabric. As one moves northward and westward in Steuben, into the deep woods, the scarification becomes more apparent. People have always logged here, but the industry has come a long way from two men pulling on a crosscut saw. Indeed, logging operations anywhere in Maine nowadays are not for nature-lovers with weak stomachs. The new logging roads, which always seem too wide and too permanent, are likely to lead to clear-cuts, which can only be described as hideous, ravaged landscapes.

Economy and Education

The loggers do well. One local woods-worker, I'm told, has recently built a brand new two-story home with a double garage. He's putting in a swimming pool. Nearly everywhere you go in Steuben these days you encounter ample evidence of unprecedented prosperity — big brand new homes, new double-wides, new lobster boats, new cars and trucks and ATVs. Steuben still has its enclaves of less fortunate, but by and large, people here seem more prosperous now than at any other time in the town's history.

Or are they? Indeed, if Steubenites are typical of Americans in general at the end of the century, they may appear to be well-off materially, but in reality, they may also be heavily in debt. One thing is certain, however: they are working, and they are spending their money. You can see it in the landscape.

While some residents commute to jobs in Ellsworth, many others thrive right here in the local economy. Indeed, everywhere you travel in

Steuben, you see evidence of folks earning a living right there: four-wheelers used for hauling clams from the mudflats, balsam brush for Christmas wreaths, and deer in November; lobster boats, draggers, skiffs, skidders, chippers, and skipjacks; tracks and paths and rutted roads snaking into dense woods and emerging along bays and blueberry barrens. The town roads are plied by a remarkable assortment of log trucks, dump trucks, refrigerated trucks, vans, and pickup trucks of all makes, models, and sizes. It's a rare family that does not own a truck of some sort. One man on the Rogers Point Road owns four cranes or boom trucks, in addition to an eclectic mix of pickups, sedans, sports cars, and sailboats. Steuben is a community where people work hard for their money, and take pride in their work. And while the townspeople continue to celebrate their rich history, they've also embraced the future. Farther down the Rogers Point Road, the local chainsaw sculptor, whose work is some of the most creative and original I've seen anywhere in Downeast Maine, has his own web site on the Internet.

In Steuben, self-employment has always commanded respect. Independent lobstermen, boat builders, carpenters, mechanics, auto body and car detailing specialists, have always been highly regarded professionals. Clam and worm diggers, pulpwood cutters, and various types of laborers are also respectable occupations, so long as one works hard at them. In Steuben, men are judged not by their credentials, educations, or titles, but by how hard they work. Most Steuben men do not want to sit behind a desk all day. And for men, especially, there seems to be little correlation here between years of formal education and annual income. On the contrary, the relationship may actually be an inverse one, as there are stories circulating about fishermen who dropped out of high school, who are now buying boats and building 200 thousand dollar homes. Meanwhile, law, teaching, and various other white collar occupations are likely to be viewed as curious and unusual ways for a local man to earn a living. According to Kunhikannan (1984, p. 218), "Of those who graduated from high school in 1978, not a single person went to college." Kunhikannan, who was then a Ph.D. student in anthropology at the State University of New York at Stony Brook, added:

> For example, two young full-time clam diggers, who had both
> finished high school, asked me how long I had been in college.
> I told them eight years. Then they asked me how much money
> I make. I told them I was working on a small scholarship and what
> my annual income came to. After that, they told me: "You're
> wasting your time. We can make that much in one summer digging

clams and raking blueberries." Then they went on to say that they had finished high school but not because they thought it would do them any good. They did it to please their parents and relatives: "If we dropped out of high school, they'd think they failed in bringing us up. My parents would be very upset if they didn't have my graduation pictures, with the caps and gown, in their living room." One of them summed up as follows: "All we need to make a good living from a town like this is a strong back and good muscles."

Kunhikannan argued that formal education had never been empha-sized in Steuben because the local economy was based primarily on har-vesting resources from the land and sea. Historically, women in Steuben have been better educated than men; in the past, they were more likely to finish high school, while today they are more apt to go on to college. Fishermen's wives were often the family bookkeepers; and of course, women typically went into nursing or teaching, professions that demand-ed formal training. Obviously, some change in attitudes has occurred since Kunhikannan did his research in the late 1970s. Residents I spoke with told me, however, that while "a few" are going on to college, the per-centage is still not high.

Conclusion

At this point in my wanderings, Steuben remains a collection of tiny closed societies, each unique and mysterious, each one a jewel ripe for the geographer's plucking. I'm not sure I really knew anything about Steuben in 1969; I'm certain I know little about it now. And that admission, more than anything else, may be reason enough to take another look.

1999

23

THE MAKING OF A RELUCTANT TRAVELER

A hair, long and black, was wrapped around a thick slab of my carne asada. I was at a cafe in Uruapan, a city in Michoacán State in west central Mexico. The restaurant was dark and intimate and quite full of locals. The meal was attractively served, the roast beef cooked to perfection. Those first few bites had been so delicious. I was starving. I hadn't eaten anything since breakfast on the ETN bus from Guadalajara. Undeterred, I removed the hair, and went right on eating. I lifted up another slab of beef with my fork, and there in a tangled web, was a second long black hair. It swirled around the meat like a meandering river and spilled out into an estuary of blood. Ugh. It sickened me. My appetite vanished. All of my anger, prejudice, and feelings of frustration about Mexico welled up inside me. I debated whether or not to bring it to the attention of the waiter. I no longer had the stomach for anything, much less a confrontation. My traveler's gloom — which had lifted in anticipation of being home with Linda and Hallie in less than a week — suddenly returned. I paid the bill and quietly left.

A large, ten-peso coin lay on the street I was about to cross. I remembered the warning — Never pick up a coin! It might be a trick. The thieves work in pairs. As you stoop down, one man pushes you from behind; his accomplice runs a knife through your ribs. I bent down to pick up the large coin, only to realize it had long ago been cemented into the pavement. A young boy saw me and smirked.

All my life I've been a reluctant traveler. I've never wanted to leave home. I almost didn't make it to kindergarten. My earliest memory of school is of my father chasing me around the side of our house as I tried to run away from the school bus. My mother ended up driving me, then sitting outside the classroom the first few days.

In V.S. Naipaul's celebrated novel, *A House for Mr. Biswas*, there is one image, more than any other in that massive, rambling narrative, that strikes a chord with me: Mohun Biswas, a humble Trinidad-born Hindu peasant, has decided to take the biggest step of his life. He will board an ocean liner for the long voyage back to India, his ancestral homeland. But at the very moment Mr. Biswas is to board the ship, fear and anxiety suddenly overcome him. He runs and hides in a stall in the men's restroom until the ship has sailed out of the harbor. At that moment, Biswas became a man close to my heart. I very likely would have done the same thing. I immediately identified with his "traveler's anxiety" because I come from a long line of reluctant travelers.

I have in my briefcase a plane ticket that I've been carrying around since 1993. The ticket has been reissued three times. I've taken several airplane trips since 1993, even two journeys to Ireland, but I can't seem to bring myself to use that particular ticket. Once, I had even packed my suitcase. I was to leave for Mexico early the next morning. But when morning came, after a mostly sleepless night, I said to Linda, "No. I'm not going to Mexico today. You know I don't like to fly during the month of May; there's likely to be thunderstorms. I'd rather stay home with you and Hallie." I didn't go. I unpacked my things and put my knapsack away. Then all the anxiety left me and I slept soundly that night.

It is not only because I do not like to fly; travel, of any mode or distance, will bring me high anxiety. I have the wanderlust, and seem to want to travel; I just can't bear to leave home. As a child I would never sleep over at a friend's house. I couldn't even imagine such a dislocation from my own bed, even for a night. I still remember the anxiety I felt on daylong field trips in elementary school. I never enjoyed them. I hated them — not so much the trip itself, but the anticipation of it. All I remember is the anxiety, and then the relief when the trip was finally over.

Many of my schoolmates went away to summer camp; but again, I wouldn't leave home. Instead, I passed my summer days exploring the woods of the East Orange Water Reserve, a large wilderness that bordered our backyard in New Jersey. It was all posted land, so I spent my boyhood as a "fugitive," hiding out in the forest. With two sisters who were much older than I, but no brothers, I was more like a shy, introverted only child. "Self-absorbed" is the word that Linda always used to describe me. Not selfish...there's a difference. The many hours of my youth spent alone in the woods of the Water Reserve most surely shaped my personality and stimulated my curiosity. I've wanted to be an explorer from my earliest recollections. According to Bruce Chatwin (1996, p. 101):

> Children need paths to explore, to take bearings on the earth
> in which they live, as a navigator takes bearings on familiar
> landmarks. If we excavate the memories of childhood, we
> remember the paths first, things and people second — paths
> down the garden, the way to school, the way round the house,
> corridors through the bracken or long grass. Tracking the paths
> of animals was the first and most important element in the
> education of early man.

But as I reflect back on my 48 years, I'm sometimes amazed at the places I haven't been — Charleston, South Carolina, for example. I've lived in South Carolina for 14 years, yet still haven't visited its most famous city. It's barely 100 miles from here! Linda's been there numerous times. She likes to travel. She doesn't share my traveler's anxiety or my high blood pressure.

We once lived in Colorado, but never got west of the Rockies. I've never been to the West Coast in the United States. We lived in North Dakota, but never saw the Badlands or the Black Hills of South Dakota. I've always talked about exploring Maine some summer, but I can't seem to leave Gouldsboro for more than a few hours. Linda sees Maine when friends and relatives visit, but I find it nearly impossible to tear myself away from our little pond.

I certainly want to travel, even though I despise it. Can you love and hate something at the same time? Evidently...because I've lived in nine states since high school (I moved to each place voluntarily) and travel seasonally between Maine and South Carolina. My affliction seems even more unusual because I am, by profession, a university-level geography professor. Still, you just can't force a reluctant traveler to travel. We invariably find ways of not arriving. I've been invited to numerous functions over the years but rarely show up for anything. You might say I've become something of an "escape" artist. Indeed, Yi-Fu Tuan (1998) begins the Preface to his book, *Escapism*, with the following proposition.

> Who hasn't — sometime — wanted to escape? But from what? To where? And once we have arrived at the good place, is this the end of the desire to move? Or does it stir again, tempted by another image, even if it be that of the place from which we started — our old home or childhood? Surely everyone has had the urge to be elsewhere in moments of stress and uncertainty. I have. Yet even though I am a geographer, whose business is to study why and how people move, as well as their ceaseless striving to make wherever they are an even better place, the word "escape" or "escapism" rarely came to the forefront of my consciousness, never offered itself as a possible key to the understanding of human nature and culture.

Back in 1989, I decided to go to a geography conference, one of a handful I've been to in my 25 year career. And since I especially despise professional meetings (they're too expensive for one thing; I'd rather spend my money doing fieldwork, looking at real geography), I thought perhaps I might enjoy it a little more if I brought Linda and Hallie along. Well, we drove to the convention city, but we were unable to find a motel that allowed pets. Finally, the desk clerk at one motel said, "We have a kennel out back."

"No. I'm afraid that won't do," I said. "She always sleeps with us. She'd be heartbroken. So would I."

Linda said, "Well, what are we going to do?"

"Let's go home!" I responded. I was elated. My anxiety was melting away.

"What about the conference?" Linda persisted.

"Who cares?" I was barely able to contain my joy. Suddenly, I was my old happy self again. I wasn't on the program; I wasn't giving a paper. Really, what did it matter? What, exactly, are those scholars trying to say, anyway? Some of it is extraordinary, fascinating, ingenious, and thought provoking; I have to admit I enjoy reading some of the scholarly journals. Some of them. But much of it is twaddle. Some of it I can't even understand. It's over my head. Or else it doesn't hold my interest. And then there are the graduate students, taking it all so seriously, wanting desperately to impress their peers, to get "published"; ultimately, to find their own place in the "ivory tower." How on earth did I ever wind up here? How indeed?

It was October! We were in southeastern Pennsylvania...in the Amish country. That's what we had come to see. That's what I have enduring memories of — the farms, the fields, the fall colors, the winding roads, the quaint Amish landscape. We eventually found a motel in a rural area far from the convention, then enjoyed the long ride home.

When I was eleven years old my biggest goal in life was to make it to the "majors" in the Millburn, New Jersey Little League. It was extremely competitive. The pressure there in suburban New Jersey to make the team, to play well, and of course, to win, was enormous. Nevertheless, I did make the majors that year and was the starting second baseman for the Eagles. But in the middle of the first game, I suddenly walked off the field. I told the coach, a kind man named Mr. Arsi, that I didn't want to play anymore. He thought I was sick. My parents came down from the stands. "I'm so nervous," I said, almost in tears. My stomach was in knots. The pressure was overwhelming. I was afraid I'd miss a ground-ball and make an error.

My parents were sympathetic. They felt that so many parents in that community put far too much pressure on their children to compete athletically and academically.

They said it was just a game; that I should just do my best and not worry about it. I was back in the lineup the next game. The following year I was named to the Millburn All-Star Team.

I competed in varsity sports all during high school and college. During my junior year of high school, I ruined my pitching arm in an amateur boxing match. The coach had told me not to box, but I ignored him. I dislocated my shoulder. I had been our number one pitcher. I let the whole team down. Baseball had meant everything to me in high school. It was the only thing I excelled at. It was my identity. Suddenly it was gone. I dealt with the loss by concentrating on long distance running.

But in college, competing against much more talented runners, I struggled for years without ever winning a varsity letter. I used to get lapped in the two-mile run. I always finished far back in the field in cross country meets. It was humiliating; it was terribly disappointing; yet oddly enough, I thoroughly enjoyed the challenge. I enjoyed thrashing myself. I trained harder. And by my junior year I was, for a while, the fifth-fastest runner on the team; that was, until I was hospitalized for asthma. The anxiety of near-success had been too much for me. The university's doctor advised the coach not to let me compete on the team anymore. So I just continued running on my own, for my own sake, on my own terms, perhaps even, as a form of escapism. No more asthma. Nearly thirty years later I was still competing in marathons.

The only time I remember my father getting really angry with me was in junior high when I brooded over losing a wrestling match. "What's the matter?" he demanded to know. "I lost today," I moaned. "You can't expect to win all the time!" It was his tone. I have the most vivid memory of that brief conversation, as if I can still feel his blood pressure rising. He was that disappointed in me. The match meant nothing; my loser's attitude was deplorable. Indeed, the game, the match, the race, even the career: I've resisted the pressure to take any of them too seriously. This has been my method — perhaps it was my father's — of putting things in perspective, of dealing with, and perhaps lessening, needless anxiety.

My father, who died of a massive heart attack at age 48, also hated to travel. My mother once told me a wonderful story about her first ride in an airplane, back in the late 1930s. She had always wanted to fly, but my father had no such inclination. One weekend, sightseeing flights were being offered at no charge at the little airport in Morristown, New Jersey, not far from my parents' home. So my mother, father, and my oldest sister, who was then a tiny baby, rode out to the airport to watch the planes take off. (I still have wonderful memories of my father taking me out to that very same airport many years later when I was a young boy. Like me, my father had a fascination with airplanes and liked to watch them take off and land.) But on this particular day in the late 1930s, my mother had said, "Oh Cliff, I'd love to go up in a plane!" Finally, my father acquiesced and said, "Okay, go ahead if you want to, but let me hold onto the baby!" That was the first of many airplane flights for my mother. But my father never would fly, and never did fly on an airplane. Perhaps he was blessed in that respect.

My father had a history of hypertension. His blood pressure was so high it kept him out of World War II. When he reported for duty the doctors thought he had taken something to elevate his blood pressure. They kept him for observation for three days but his blood pressure never did go down. Finally, they just sent him home.

And it bothered him that he'd missed the war. Several times, he had said to me, "I've always felt like I missed something." Even then — I was in my early teens when he first told me this — I could sense his regret. Of course he missed something! It was the defining moment for his generation. But this admission, perhaps more than anything my father ever said to me, brought me especially close to him. Like all men, he carried within him certain insecurities and vulnerabilities. He showed me his human side. He confided in me his greatest regret; this troubling mixture of relief in not having to leave his family and go off to war; yet at the same time, disappointment, and perhaps even guilt, for having missed out on something that was larger than life.

My father died on the last night of our vacation in Maine during July of 1966. We had planned to drive over 500 miles to our home in New Jersey the following morning. No doubt, the anxiety of the upcoming road trip had elevated his blood pressure (it always does it for me) and probably triggered his heart attack. I remember waking in the middle of the night and hearing men's voices. The door to my bedroom was open just a crack. I could barely see the metal frame of a gurney as they struggled to move my father down the narrow staircase. I had to have known my father was seriously ill. I had to have known that this was real and not a dream...but I never got up. I stayed in bed. I remained paralyzed by fear. I had never seen my father really sick before. He never missed a day of work. I somehow willed myself back to sleep, as if I thought I could wake up and find that it really had been a dream, that my father was fine. He wasn't. In the morning, my mother came in and said, "Daddy's gone, Al." I never even said goodbye.

Traveling was a relatively new form of anxiety for my father. During the first two decades of their marriage, my mother said that my father had seemed quite content to use his vacations to read, paint the house, or putter around the yard with his three dogs. He never wanted to go anywhere, at least not any place far away. I can remember my mother suggesting places 15 to 20 miles distant, and my father saying, "What do you want to go way out there for? It's so far from here!"

Sometime in the mid 1950s, my parents tried taking a week's vacation at the Jersey shore. But Ace, my father's beloved Great Dane who had been left behind in a kennel, stopped eating. The nervous kennel owner telephoned us at the beach. My father hurried home to be with his dog. Ace was a one-man dog. When my father went to work he'd just lie down and sulk. My mother would bring him his food dish but he wouldn't even acknowledge her. Only after she left would he come out of his dog house and eat his dinner. My father took it especially hard when Ace died. The Great Dane's passing, however, made it possible for us to go on New England vacations as our other two dogs, a mutt and her pup that my father had found tied to the railroad tracks, would at least continue to eat when we were away. "Your father loved anything with four legs," my mother has always said. She had a heck of a time getting him to leave his dogs and go anywhere, but once he got there he usually enjoyed himself.

My father really didn't need to travel. He got all of the intellectual stimulation he needed from books. I envy him that. Seated in his special easy chair, his feet on his hassock with his dogs at his side, my father, when reading, was truly at peace. His serenity filled the room. Books and newspapers were stacked on the little stand next to his chair, on the radiator, and on the floor around him. I remember him placing me on his lap and teaching me my first words and letters, long before I ever went to school. Cat — "c" "a" "t," and then he had me repeat the letters — was the first printed word he taught me. It was as if he couldn't wait for me to begin school.

The public library was one of the first places I remember my father taking me. We went every Monday night. I remember him leading me downstairs to the children's section where I selected my first books. I can still see their spines in the metal bookshelves. I can still see the basement room, the tiled floor, the stairs leading down. We would then go upstairs, and while my father perused the stacks and selected his books, I would sit in a big overstuffed chair in the large reading room. I'd sit in front of the fireplace and try to get started on one of my books, but mostly I'd just stare at the large oil painting on the wall above. It was a Western scene at dusk. Indians squatted around a blazing campfire. I especially remember the vivid oranges and reds in the painting. It made me want to go out West and camp out under the stars. I loved that painting. There was something about that landscape that made me, a boy from suburban New Jersey, long for the wide open spaces.

After my father had checked out his books, we'd then go across the street to a little newspaper and tobacco shop where he always bought me a candy bar, a creamsickle, or an Eskimo Pie, a few cigars, or some pipe tobacco for himself, and of course, a big fat New York newspaper. My father and I never went anywhere without stopping off for a treat. He knew the names of all the candy bars, and at one time or another, he had tried them all. It was the same way with ice cream and different ethnic foods. He liked to try everything. My father loved to indulge himself, as well as my mother and me. She'd always tell him as we left the house: "Don't buy him a lot of junk, Cliff." But he always did. He wasn't over-weight, but he never went past a "candy store," as he called them, without buying us a treat, and of course, his New York paper.

My father read all the major newspapers of the New York-New Jersey area — the *Times*, *The Herald Tribune*, *The Newark Evening News*, *The Star Ledger*. He read them critically and religiously. He had definite opinions about them too, and always joked about which ones were "terri-ble," or "absolutely awful." As a boy, I used to love to ask him about the merits of various newspapers, just to hear his colorful commentary. I can only imagine the enjoyment we would have had discussing the merits of newspapers and journalists and writers today.

My father was in love with the printed word. He seemed especially happy rummaging around used bookstores and library sales. We were always lugging home paper bags of old books. His tastes were eclectic — biographies, novels, histories, atlases, classics. He especially liked Dickens. But I also remember him showing me a history of the United States by a writer by the name of Gordy. It was published around 1920, but my father admired it, and turned its pages with a special reverence that he held for writers and scholars.

I don't know if my father ever wrote anything himself. Maybe he did-n't feel comfortable writing. I don't ever remember him even writing a letter. I have no recollection of his handwriting. My mother always took care of the finances, so I have no memory even of his signature on a check.

It is with inconsolable sadness that I write about my father. He had always wanted me to become a teacher...I think...because he would have liked to have been one himself. What a splendid teacher he would have made! But like most working-class men of his generation, he never had the money nor the opportunity to attend college. Since age 17, he had always worked in a General Motors ballbearing plant. (He had worried back then, in the mid-sixties, about the plant possibly closing. He had mentioned the possibility of being transferred to Sandusky, Ohio. The plant did close a few years after he died, and the production jobs, no doubt, were outsourced to areas of cheaper labor, like Mexico.) I had just turned 15 when my father died, so I really wasn't old enough to appreciate all of his talents. My mother said he could play the piano by ear. I know his ear for language — for nuance, tone, and subtlety — had to have been extraordinary. He was kind and patient and sympathetic; he was an exceptionally keen and sensitive listener — those were qualities that people especially admired about him.

It was my mother who traveled to Maine alone on a Greyhound Bus in 1959 to meet with a realtor and eventually buy a house. Were it not for my mother's spirit of adventure, I probably would never have known Maine, or any other new place, for that matter. I have long thought that people who grow up in mostly urbanized places like New Jersey are among the world's most provincial people. Research has shown that New Yorkers, especially, carry around highly inaccurate and distorted mental maps of what the rest of the country is like.

As much as I had wanted to move from an increasingly urbanizing New Jersey to rural Maine after my father died in 1966, it took me most of my sophomore year of high school to make the adjustment. I was so shy, so reclusive. Then, as now, I was quite antisocial. I didn't especially want to meet new people. I had never slept over at a friend's house, had never gone to parties or school dances. Sports, especially baseball, enabled me to eventually make friends in high school. Later, I went out for the cross country team. In the meantime, I retreated into my own world. I no longer had the Water Reserve; I now had some place even better — the Maine woods and the bay. I fished for trout. I became a skilled hunter of rabbits and grouse. I learned to dig clams and manage a round-bottomed skiff in the bay. So that by my senior year, I was at home, both in school and in our little Downeast community...so much so, that I've often wondered why I ever left.

But I had also inherited my mother's wanderlust, and in 1969, set off on a 350cc Yamaha motorcycle, all the way to Arkansas, where I attended college. I doubt I would have done anything like that had my father been alive. He wouldn't have wanted me to go. He wouldn't have wanted me to have a motorcycle. Unlike my mother, he was a worrier, and I would not have been able to put him through such anxiety. His untimely passing inadvertently allowed me more freedom. And after much arguing, I was eventually able to convince my mother to let me ride the motorcycle to Arkansas.

The motorcycle came to me naturally. The strange little machine, with its whining two-stroke engine, seemed to have been designed for a lone wanderer like me. I had no interest in automobiles. And I would never have gone there on an airplane. I needed the physical experience of the journey itself. It also bolstered my self-confidence.

It was the year I met Linda. I fell head over heels for her the fall of my freshman year. A few months later, it was the bike that saved me.

And it's a good thing...because Linda dumped me. "I think I need to date other people," she had said. She was a year older than I, a sophomore. We'd known each other for three glorious months. This was in late January of 1970, right before the first semester exams. I remember being at a restaurant with some guys in the dorm, going into the restroom and vomiting my guts out. I was devastated. I thought she was gone from my life forever.

I had to get away, far away. We had a week's break before the start of the spring semester, so I packed a few clothes in a canvas duffel bag, tied it to the sissy bar and headed south out of town. The clock at the bank read two thirty-five; the temperature 27 degrees. I was going to Mexico! A friend on the track team was flying home to Mission, Texas in the lower Rio Grande Valley. "I'll be down in about two days," I said. "Yeah, right."

It was more than 700 miles from Magnolia, Arkansas to Mission, Texas. I rode all night, into northwest Louisiana, then into east Texas. I remember stopping after midnight and being so cold that I wrapped my arms around the hot engine block. I took off my gloves and nearly burned my hands trying to thaw them out. A few hours before daylight, I pulled into a roadside park and huddled on the ground in a tight ball next to my bike and tried to sleep. Daylight came. Then it started to rain.

The state police pulled me over on the interstate outside of Houston. I was going 70 miles-an-hour in the pouring rain. The two troopers asked me where I was going, shook their heads, then told me to slow down. I thanked them for stopping me. Even then, at age 18, I realized how perilously close I'd come to the edge.

It had warmed up to 70 degrees when I turned on to Ragland Road in Mission, Texas and pulled up at my friend's trailer house. The sunshine was dazzling. There were oranges hanging off the trees in the dooryard. "I can't believe you really made it!" my friend kept saying. "And on that damn Yamaha! Nobody from college has ever been down here." "Show me on the map where your home is," his mother insisted. When I pointed to the easternmost county in the United States, my friend said, "Gosh Al, you and me live at the opposite ends of the country!" Had he just now realized that?

I ate my first Mexican food at a nearby bowling alley that evening. It's funny, but all these years later, I can still smell that place, and the Tex-Mex food that was being served. My friend tricked me into biting into my first ever jalapeño pepper, then told me about all the stomach operations his father had endured from a lifetime of eating hot, spicy foods. We rode the Yamaha over the border the next day, and I saw for the first time the strange new world I've been trying to comprehend ever since. And a few days later, when I pulled out of Mission and headed back to Arkansas, I was wearing aviator sunglasses and a fringe leather jacket like Dennis Hopper wore in the movie *Easy Rider*.

And those boys in the dorm from small-town Arkansas — dull, retarded societies with names like Hatfield, Homer, Hope, and Horatio — were really impressed. Adventure to them was getting a six-pack and cruising the Sonic Drive-in. "Never thought you'd really do it! All the way to Mexico and back on that Yamaha!" I hadn't gotten over Linda — not at all — but travel, especially the adventurous kind, has a way of opening up new worlds and putting one's life into perspective. If I could survive this perilous journey, I could survive almost anything.

My freshman year of college was unquestionably the most exciting year of my life. I rode the Yamaha to a football game in Durant, Oklahoma in October; rode to New Orleans for Thanksgiving; to Mexico for semester break; and during spring break, I rode to Galveston and camped out on the beach. I ran cross country in the fall. In February, I tried out for the football team as a walk-on during spring training, but nearly got my head knocked off. Then I tried out for baseball, but my throwing arm had never recovered from the high school boxing mishap, so I ended up running track. My grades were barely high enough to keep me off academic probation. But at least by the end of the spring semester Linda and I were dating again.

I rode the bike back to Maine that May, and just six miles short of home, I was pulled over by the state police. "Sixty-eight in a fifty-five," the officer said. "Let me see your license." But as I tried to get off my bike I slipped in the loose sand on the highway's shoulder, lost my balance and fell into the bushes with the Yamaha on top of me. "Are you alright?" the rattled policeman asked, as he lifted the machine off my legs. "Yeah, I'm just dead tired. I've ridden all the way from Arkansas." "Welcome home." This time I was handed a speeding ticket.

In 1971, I bought my first car, a 1964 Volvo. It was 25 years before I got on a motorcycle again. Suddenly, in my mid-forties, I began to see my life for what it is — like writing, it needs to be kept so simple so as to be transparent. Indeed, perhaps a man that is whole needs only three things: the love of a good woman (or friend), a good dog, and a good motorcycle...a pair of running shoes, a plane ticket, a good book, or some other means of escape. Women are domesticators and nurturers; men are hunters and wanderers, so the anthropologists tell us. Unlike my father, I have to travel. My life will remain incomplete...unfulfilled, unless I explore other worlds. Looking back, maybe that's the lesson the Yamaha taught me; what the Mexican odyssey was teaching me now.

But what was I doing in Arkansas? Of all the places I could have gone to college, I chose Magnolia, Arkansas. The only way I can explain it is that I'm sometimes drawn to certain places for reasons that I cannot adequately explain. Well-intentioned people have always given me advice, too, which I've invariably ignored. Instead, I've always followed my instincts and gone and done what I've wanted.

Still, everything I've done, everywhere I've gone — all have been with reluctance, with much trepidation. I never even wanted to get married, and on my wedding day, I asked my mother if she thought I was doing the right thing. Such reluctance, and after six years of courtship! And, of course, I've never wanted any children, only a dog.

How, indeed, does one become such a reluctant traveler? Perhaps it's in the genes. Perhaps it's in the collective memory of generations past.

During the winter of 1912, my grandmother, who was then in her thirties and living in West Hartlepool, England, learned suddenly that her husband, a sea captain, had been lost in a storm. They never found his ship. Naturally, my grandmother was grief stricken; she went into a deep depression and thought that her life was over. But my aunt, her sister, also had the wanderlust. And after much prodding, she convinced my grandmother that come April they should get away for a while...that they should sail to America on the maiden voyage of the Titanic. But my grandmother, a most reluctant traveler, had procrastinated too long. By the time they got down to Southhampton, the Titanic had sailed. They missed the boat! They sailed to America on the very next ship to leave England after the Titanic. They were already at sea when the Titanic went down. Both women ended up marrying Americans and neither ever went back to England, even for a visit.

As a young boy, I could never understand why my grandmother, who also died during the summer of 1966, never wanted to go home. She loved England, and never lost her accent or her British ways. She always referred to my father as "His Lordship." And I can remember asking my mother, many times, "Why doesn't Grandma go back to England? At least for a visit? Why hasn't she ever wanted to go home to see her family and the house where she grew up?" I don't exactly remember what my mother's explanation was. It doesn't matter. I now understand.

2000

24

THE DAY OF THE DEAD

There was always a mound of yesterday's garbage in the southeast corner of the plaza when I began my morning run in Pátzcuaro, a town in Michoacán State in the volcanic mountains of West Central Mexico. A shrunken old woman, wrapped in her blue rebozo and holding a sturdy nylon shopping bag would arrive and begin picking through the pile. After a few laps around the plaza, I'd notice her bag would be full, then off she'd go. The dogs would then move in, but not for long, because a second old woman would soon appear to see what she could find. Both her size and appearance were strikingly similar to the first woman, and as I continued to run my laps, one scavenger seemed to become another, until I suddenly realized they were gone and the dogs had taken over.

Usually, there were two dogs. Once, I had seen as many as eight. One had a white fringe and skirt, in contrast to its black coat, and an abundance of whiskers on its long muzzle, which made me wonder if it was part-Collie and part-Airedale. Many of the dogs are pretty good-sized up here in the mountains, with thick coats to see them through the highland winter. The garbage men arrived next, shooing away the dogs; with flat shovels, they quickly scraped up the last of the trash heap, which was somewhat smaller now that the scavengers had done their work.

In another corner of the plaza, a wizened old man with a long, gray beard and long, gray scraggly locks of hair streaming out from underneath a battered cowboy hat, and clad in a dirty poncho, jogged in place each time I ran past. He was barefoot. The temperature was probably in the high forties. A much younger man hollered, "vamos! vamos! vamos!" But most people strolling across the plaza or sitting on the concrete benches soaking up the morning sun as it rose above the blue-gray volcanic mountains paid little attention to me.

One chilly morning, a tall dark Mexican woman, her thick black hair in a long braid, suddenly emerged about fifty yards ahead of me. She was a strong runner, and it took me five or six painful laps to finally pull alongside and eventually overtake her. But then she surged! And for about three more laps, round and round the quarter-mile-long plaza, we ran faster and faster, until I finally pulled well ahead and heard her go "whew!" I ran another hard lap, then slowed to a jog. And as the Mexican woman ran by, I smiled and said, "Buenos dias," and gave her the thumbs-up. She beamed and said, "Si! Si!" Perhaps a half hour later, after I had showered and had reemerged on the plaza, I noticed that she was still out there...running...then stretching...then jumping rope.

In 1991, Mexican runners surprised the world by finishing first and second in the New York City Marathon. On that same day, another Mexican runner won the Marine Corps Marathon in Washington, D.C. The Africans, as usual, had been favored to win in New York. I watched the race on television, and all the media attention seemed to be focused on the Africans, who had been training in the Rocky Mountains of the western United States. None of the experts even mentioned the Mexican runners. But at 17 miles into the race, it was Salvador Garcia, a Mexican, who surged to the front of the pack. Arturo Barios, another Mexican, soon appeared in second place. The Africans fell several yards behind; the first finisher from the United States was back about twentieth. From that year on, Mexicans have figured prominently in long distance running. They are now among the best in the world.

There is no heat in the hotels in Pátzcuaro. I slept (or tried to sleep) with my socks on beneath four heavy woolen blankets. Much of Michoacán is tierra fria (cold land), and during the winter, night-time temperatures can drop below freezing. I've spent winters in cold places — Colorado, Maine, North Dakota — but in some respects, winter seems harder in Mexico. There is no thermostat to flick on, no woodstove to stoke. People here simply bundle up at night, then come out into the sun to warm up in the morning. Mexicans are great sweater wearers. And in the cool of evening, after the tropical sun had dipped back down below the mountains, I'd notice groups of people sitting outdoors at small, intimate tables drinking expresso and talking.

So every morning, as Pátzcuaro awakened, and people came out into the sun to warm up, I'd run my laps around the plaza. I grew to enjoy it, especially the feeling of cameradery and neighborliness that came from sharing the morning sun with the locals. At more than seven thousand feet above sea level, it's not easy to run here. The footing is difficult too — the hexagonal tiles have been worn down and pitted in places; I had to be careful how I planted my feet. But there were usually a handful of dedicated Mexican runners and joggers, so I was rarely alone. And as I gasped and sucked in the cold mountain air, I imagined that the altitude would have the same effect on me as it had on Garcia and Barios: I would run like the wind when I returned to sea level!

In early February a chilly winter drizzle fell over the town of Pátzcuaro. Big, puffy clouds and a yellow ochre sky shone in the late afternoon after the rain had stopped. Pátzcuaro is a strange, mystical place where you always hear the shrillest-sounding songbirds, their melodies emanating from the open windows of people's homes, as you walk its cobblestone streets. It's a charming adobe hill town, but how dull it must be to actually live here.

The desk clerk at my hotel had just returned after living in southern California for eleven years. She was in her twenties, attractive, and had a four-year-old son who suffered from asthma and related bronchial problems. She complained that the cold mountain air was making the boy's health worse. The boy's father still lived in California. He didn't know she was here. He wouldn't help her with the finances anyway, she said. She wasn't married to this man and hoped he'd never find her.

"He was too possessive. And he was always jealous. He didn't want me to work or have a career. I never went out. I never left the house. Latino men are like that. They aren't like Anglos. Anglo men let their wives have their own careers. They help them raise the kids. Latino men want their wives to stay home, do all the housework, raise kids, never go out. I didn't want that...so I left him.

"I moved to L.A. in 1981. I hardly spoke any English. The teacher at the elementary school I went to — a black woman — didn't teach us anything. That first year...all she did was show us the same videos over and over. The next year, I got a better teacher and I started learning English. But it was hard for me.

"A lot of Latinos in California won't even help their own people. They wouldn't help me learn English. Their attitude was that they had to learn it on their own...they weren't going to help other Mexicans learn it. I don't think that's right. I think we've all got to help each other."

I rode buses nearly every day I spent in Pátzcuaro. The daily bus ride in Michoacán was a ritual I found hard to pass up. All I had to do was walk out to the highway and hail one. One day, when I had to wait an hour to get a bus to Cherán, I had a chance to observe the street life at a nondescript intersection of Pátzcuaro's busy perimeter road and another road leading into town. A little eatery across the street sold roasted chickens; it also doubled as a bar. Adjacent to the eatery was a dusty cobblestone road leading uphill to the El Estribo volcano. A couple of young boys rode horses bareback over the cobblestones. Younger boys peddled up and down the dusty road on bicycles with tiny back wheels. Five young men sat on the stoop of the chicken restaurant the hour or so I waited. Such idleness here! Didn't they have anything better to do? How does one survive when there is little or no employment? Crime? I doubt it. They certainly didn't pay any attention to me. I had hundreds of dollars of cash on my body. I didn't have any allies here; still, I might as well have been invisible. The idle young men just talked and laughed amongst themselves; they didn't even look over at me. No whistles or catcalls.

Whereas I sometimes felt uneasy waiting on streetcorners in Mexico City, I felt no such anxiety in Michoacán. I'm not sure why, but a decade-long experience here convinced me that idle young men in Michoacán were harmless, that people were kind and decent, that I could explore and wander anywhere I wanted without ever being threatened or robbed. Naive? Maybe. Dangerous? Possibly. But I still think it's safe.

The street was also home to a collection of stray mongrels. I watched one pathetic little creature with a hurt paw limp across the road in front of traffic. Two other mutts — one with thick, matted black and white hair, the other just brown — nipped at the poor little cripple. All three dogs eventually settled down beneath a parked truck. Meanwhile, buses of various companies, models, and vintages roared past, belching black fumes. The occasional private car — usually an inexpensive Chrysler model or an older Japanese sedan — taxis, and motorbikes buzzed along. The street was never quiet. And in spite of the strong winds that stirred up clouds of dust that irritated my eyes, the fumes from all the passing vehicles never seemed to dissipate.

People were always crossing; there was a steady stream of men, women, and children padding up and down the dusty perimeter road. They trudged past the row of auto repair places — a nondescript landscape of black grease and oil-blackened dirt, the concrete shop fronts themselves painted in bright orange and yellow, advertising engines and transmissions and tires. Men in dirty tee-shirts threw buckets of water out on the parched earth, trying to keep the dust down. After all, this is also a residential area. It is indeed amazing how many Mexicans inhabit landscapes that seem almost invisible because of their nondescriptness. Meanwhile, a young man approached me needing money for the bus fare to Morelia. I didn't have change, so I gave him five pesos. He thanked me and shook my hand.

I may not have found my way in this Mexican culture as a problem-solving scholar, armed with a sound methodology and state-of-the-art research tools, but what does it matter? We can't all be specialists at everything. Is there no room in this world for amateurs anymore? Not necessarily experts, or scholars, but people who just like to walk and look. I wonder if we don't have something worthwhile to say about this landscape of decay and disorder that some of the experts might have omitted. Could an examination of this nondescript landscape devoted mostly to the maintenance of automobiles possibly reveal more about the Mexican culture and condition than something more obvious like the market, the plaza, the cathedral, or the ruins? Perhaps, because the automobile has altered and degraded the Mexican landscape profoundly.

A man with only one arm emerged from an auto repair shop. His hand and arm were coated in black grease. He smiled warmly at me. From behind I had imagined him to be in his late fifties. From the front, his face appeared younger, perhaps late thirties. How did he manage the wrenches? How much of a disadvantage is it for a mechanic to have only one hand, one arm? I tried to imagine how difficult his life might be. Why couldn't he be fitted with an artificial limb like a former classmate of mine who had lost his arm in a factory accident? Perhaps my answer lay in the dust and desolation of the street.

At last, a bus appeared whose handwritten sign on the front windshield read: Cherán. It was a minibus operated by Autobuses Occidente — big enough to seat 15-20 people comfortably. But for much of the journey into the pine-covered sierra, Indians continued to board, until the center aisle was jam packed with standing passengers.

Early in the journey an elderly Indian woman got on board, lugging a large plastic bucket full of fish and a burlap sack bulging with pottery. How strong these Purépechan women are! But when she tried to drag the sack down the aisle it got jammed next to my seat. I reached down and lifted the sack free, but as I hauled it up an exquisite piece of pottery dropped out and smashed to pieces on the metal bus floor. I wondered whether I should offer to pay for it. I felt bad about it, but I didn't want to make things worse by insulting her. She was old but also very dignified. She just smiled and moved down the aisle without saying a word.

The bus driver, a young man in his late teens or early twenties, seemed to love North American pop music. He had the volume on his tape player turned up loud enough to burst an eardrum. But I rather enjoyed it. The loud rock music seemed quite appropriate on this rattletrap Mexican bus full of Indians as we wound our way up the one lane mountain road. At that moment I couldn't have been happier. I was, once again, a man in motion, an explorer with a destination. The weather was perfect — clear and crisp — the scenery, which shifted continually from pine-covered mountains to open meadows to small villages, was dramatic. The only thing that bothered me was the garbage along the roadside. No matter where you go in Mexico there are buses, and wherever the buses go there is roadside litter. People eat constantly on these buses, and when they are finished, they toss the refuse out the windows. Much of the litter is plastic, everything from soda pop containers to Pampers.

We descended into a narrow valley where scores of tiny, unpainted wooden plank houses clustered tightly together. The houses had hip-roofs made of pine shakes. A sign read SEVINA — population 3,000. Sevina was a tiny dot on my detailed map of Michoacán. Three thousand people!

Thousands of nucleated settlements with millions of inhabitants dot Mexico's landscape. They've inhabited these valleys for thousands of years.

But the Purépechan plank house is an introduction, traced back to German miners, who first came here in the 1700s. There's a single door in front and a porch with a roof overhang. The thick pine planks are laid horizontally one atop the other and notched at the ends. Many of the plank houses have elaborate woodcarving on the doors, corner posts, and eaves. The porch is likely to be adorned with rows of potted geraniums. Although they are sometimes painted, the wood is usually left to weather a dark gray.

The minibus crept through Sevina on a road that was just rocks and dust. The village consisted mostly of walled compounds, each containing an assortment of chickens, pigs, mules, horses, dogs, and children. I would have liked to have gotten off the bus and looked around a bit, but I was afraid I'd be stranded here.

Half an hour later, we reached Cherán, a large Purépechan Indian town at the intersection of two main roads, where I abandoned the bus and its earsplitting music. Cherán is perched on the side of a volcano. School had just let out for the siesta. It was one o'clock. School children toting book satchels romped in the plaza — running, laughing, making fun of me, kicking soccer balls on their way home for dinner. Mexican towns, like U.S. towns, always seem happiest when school lets out. In 1946, an anthropologist named Ralph Beals suggested that: "Although Cherán, like many other towns of the Purépechan area, is thought of and thinks of itself as Indian, it is difficult to identify anything that is aboriginal besides its language and racial type. Cherán's domesticated animals, many of its crops, its patterns of cultivation, and its general technologies and material culture are almost exclusively European."

Today, in Cherán, like in nearly every other town in Michoacán, you're likely to encounter California, Oregon, Texas, North Carolina, even Maine license plates. There are still plenty of farmers and wood-carvers here, but Michoacán is largely a remittance economy. Slightly more than one-half of its adult population (2 million, compared to 1.9 million who remain in Michoacán) lives and works in the United States. And in spite of the difficulty and expense involved in crossing the U.S. border (about $1,200 to hire a "coyote" to smuggle you across) the migration is stronger than ever. It began long before the financial crisis of the 1990s; it will probably continue long after. For Michoacános, migration has become a way of life. When boys reach seventeen or eighteen they simply go north. Many small towns in the state are dominated by women, children, and the elderly. It is estimated that these young men send back about a billion dollars a year in remittances.

Much of the farmland in Michoacán was once held by wealthy landowners. But in the 1930s, President Lazaro Cardenas, a native of Michoacán, confiscated the land and redistributed it among the peasantry. Each family received eight to sixteen acres, depending on the quality of the land. Over the years, those parcels of land had to be divided again and again, as families grew. You cannot make a decent living on a tiny plot of land anymore, so many young men began going north, or else to Mexico City. Under the Ejido System of land redistribution, Mexican peasants were not permitted to rent or sell their land. So the elderly, and often the women, stayed put, hoping that relief would come in the form of remittances from their children or relatives.

In recent years, the Mexican government has changed the law, making it possible for ejido-holders to rent or sell their plots, in the hope that farmland can be kept in production. The plan is not working. The 1930s ideal of the small peasant farmer seems to have lost its appeal. More young people are leaving now than ever before. Indeed, the land is sometimes sold to pay for the journey north.

Occasionally, in little towns like Cherán, one suddenly encounters a nice new house that stands out because of its size or modern style. You might also see a brand new vehicle in the driveway, perhaps a new satellite dish in the yard. These are usually indications of remittances sent from the United States.

In the beginning, Michoacános typically come home for Christmas and perhaps even stay the winter. Eventually, the visits home become less frequent, until finally, some don't make it home at all. There is a road outside Aiken, South Carolina named Michoacán Lane. All of its residents hail from this impoverished Mexican state. Michoacán has become a tortured land of tearful partings, and all-too-brief, but joyful reunions. What role, I wonder, does peer pressure play in this migration? Young men go away, only to return as relatively prosperous heroes. But what about those who really do not want to leave their homes? Would they feel as though they had failed as men if they stayed behind? Possibly. One gets the impression that for many young men here, the journey north is a rite of passage.

I walked around Cherán for a while in the hot sun. It was almost too dazzling for good photography, but it didn't matter; because of the steepness of the terrain, it was hard to get good shots; the perspective was all wrong. I was either looking straight up at something perched on the mountainside, or else I was looking for miles off in the distance at volcanoes rising from brown, dusty fields. I eventually walked down the road and out to the edge of town to take in the vista. I snapped a few photographs of the cinder cone in the valley. A man led a horse towing a single, heavy wooden plank down the road ahead of me. Such inefficiency here. Men could waste the day on what seemed like meaningless tasks. Dusty trails snaked down the mountainside to tiny houses in the valley. The air smelled of dung and mules and horses. The roadside was strewn with plastic litter. Except for the sound of a motor off in the distance, all was quiet.

Not wanting to be stranded in Cherán, I anxiously boarded another, larger bus, also second class, to Uruapan, that would take me through Paracho, the little town where they make fine guitars. Main Street was lined with tiny shops where guitars hung from the ceilings.

A woman towing a grimy little boy with long, dirty fingernails sat in the seat beside me. He sat in her lap eating cookies out of a cellophane bag and stared at me. I didn't feel like engaging them. I just sensed that this poor woman would have been most uncomfortable if I had, so I just looked out the window. It was a slow ride through the pine-covered mountains and avocado groves as we approached Uruapan. The bus was wearing on me. It would be another three hours or more before I'd get back to Pátzcuaro. I had to change buses in Uruapan; then it was a slow ride of almost two hours over the mountains into Pátzcuaro. Sometimes I wondered why I put myself through it — one second-class bus was as dirty and demoralizing as another. But it was the theater; each day I'd get up and be drawn to them, as if I didn't dare miss out on another experience, another landscape or human drama.

That evening, I went to mass at the Basilica in Pátzcuaro. It was being restored. The deterioration of the ceiling — the peeling paint and wallpaper — wasn't evident on my earlier trips. Everything grows old and deteriorates, including me. There was scaffolding high up into the nave, then a net of wire mesh to catch the falling debris. Work had stopped for the day and mass went on as usual. There might have been a hundred or so parishioners this Friday night. I prayed for Linda and Hallie and for both of our families. I prayed for my own health and safety. A black, flatcoat setter dog slept in the doorway of the Basilica when I stepped out into the dark, starlit night. I stopped momentarily and looked closely at the dog — just to make certain it wasn't Hallie, just to be sure I really was here.

A drunken man sat beside me on the bus ride back from Quiroga next morning. I had gone there to buy a leather briefcase for Linda. Quiroga, 12 miles north of Pátzcuaro, is on the highway between Morelia and

Zamora. Its main street is lined with leather shops. Of all the empty seats on the bus, the drunk had to choose this one. And he was a nuisance. He clutched a can of Modelo Beer and said, "Aqui! Bebe Si?" I smiled, and declined as pleasantly as I could. He kept turning around to the young men a couple of seats back, grinning at them, as if seeking their approval. It was all rather pathetic, as if he were showing them: "Look at what we've got here — A GRINGO! Ha! Ha! Ha!" Most of his front teeth were missing. He had long greasy hair and wore an even grimier-looking baseball cap. I would guess he was in his late thirties or early forties, but I couldn't tell. His old woolen jacket and worn striped pants of the early seventies style were also dirty. I was squeamish about his pant leg rubbing up against mine. He stank, too, of body odor and stale beer.

The drunken man kept poking me in the ribs, asking me all sorts of questions. Where was I from? Which hotel was I staying at? Had I been to Zirahúen? That's where he was from. There was a beautiful lake there. I said, yes, I had seen it. I agreed, it was beautiful. I was lying. I had never been there. He asked me the time. I noticed he was wearing a watch.

A seat became vacant a few rows forward. Should I take it? I didn't want to insult him, or make him angry. I decided to stay put. I looked out the window as much as possible and tried to ignore him. After a while, he became tranquil. Maybe the alcohol was making him sleepy. I hoped and prayed that he'd exit the bus before we got to Pátzcuaro. The last thing I wanted was to have him following me to my hotel.

Just before we turned on to the perimeter road that circles Pátzcuaro my prayers were answered. He suddenly got up, then politely said "Goodbye" in English. He was, evidently, going to wait for a connecting bus to Zirahúen. I glanced out the window as we pulled away and noticed him shuffling around amongst the eucalyptus trees, searching for a little cover in order to relieve himself. I turned around to the young men in the seats behind me and smiled. We all laughed.

In the Basilica that Sunday evening, I watched a group of women and children drop to their knees, then slowly creep along on the cold stone floor, all the way to the altar. A young mother and her two daughters went first. The youngest girl, who might have been seven, moved along easily and rapidly, well ahead of her mother and sister. She seemed to be showing off. Her little body moved with sheer delight. Not so for the middle-aged women that followed the mother and two daughters; for them it was a struggle, a marathon of sorts, slowly paying out in their facial expressions as they got closer and closer to the altar. Such reverence!

Adjacent to my pew was a long, glass-covered casket containing a plaster statue of a reclining Jesus. A young couple with four children went up to the casket and touched the glass, as if they were trying to touch Jesus himself. Then they touched their own faces and blessed themselves. Another couple, this one with an infant and two toddlers, put their hands to the glass, then they rubbed their hands against their tiny children's faces. Such faith! Is it faith in God? Is it superstition? Is it some sort of peasant belief in the power of statues and idols? Why don't I, as a life-long practicing Catholic, have a similar belief in the power of symbols? Am I so arrogant as to actually believe I know more about the true meaning of Christianity than this peasant family? Or is my belief that such idol worship is foolish and a sign of ignorance, another example of gringo snobbery? What, essentially, is Catholicism about? Isn't it really about faith? And whose faith is stronger, the supposedly sophisticated gringo, or the dirt-poor Mexican peasant?

That evening, I went down to the only leather shop on the plaza and bought a leather jacket. I had looked at dozens of similar jackets in Quiroga, but the choice was too overwhelming; I came away without buying anything. Here, I just grabbed one of a half-dozen. It fit, so I bought it. But when I got the jacket to my hotel room, I noticed a slight blemish or flaw just below the collar. It's not a perfect world. Everything is flawed in some way. That morning I had been in more than 20 leather goods shops and came away without a jacket. Only when the selection had been pared down did I find one that suited me. Only it was flawed. I will treasure it forever.

The flaw in my prized leather jacket reminded me of the pain and anguish I had experienced when my first book was published in 1993. I had worked on it for nearly five years. I wanted it to be perfect. The manuscript I submitted to the publisher was nearly flawless. Two of my colleagues had helped me with the editing. But when it was finally published there were more than 60 errors, mostly typographical. Most of the errors were ones that I had already corrected on the galleys. The people who had done the computer work were young, underpaid, and careless. The book meant nothing to them. I was devastated. I had wanted so much for the book to be perfect. It was an embarrassment, a humiliation; I lay on my back and felt ill.

And now, alone in that freezing hotel room in Pátzcuaro, wearing my flawed leather jacket for warmth, not show, I thought: We always strive for perfection in our world — at least the little bit of it we think we can control — but we never achieve it. Everything in this world is flawed in some way. And as I reflect on my publication of 1993, it is the book itself — not just the typos or computer errors — that is flawed. Like this manuscript, it was written by a struggling writer. It was written by a man who was trying to find his way, both in the culture he was writing about, and in the writing craft itself. The publisher, his assistants, the writer himself — all needed to be forgiven...I needed to just let it go.

And that, I believe, was the message that was meant for me that evening in the Basilica, when I watched those young families touching the glass case that contained the statue of the reclining Jesus. Everything in the Basilica was once touched by humans — the gold leaf, the marble, the painted woodwork. Now some of the gold leaf was flaking off, the paint peeling. I had examined the wooden pews; no doubt, those were flawed as well. And of course, I am flawed in so many ways, as were those people touching the glass case and asking for God's blessing. Forgiveness — that's what Jesus stressed; not perfection. That poor, drunken soul on the bus from Quiroga — he needed forgiveness; he needed my prayers. I began to wonder what his life was like. Did he have a home, a wife, children? I thought of my own wife, my dog, our home. I had a lot to be thankful for, perhaps more than he. I was glad I hadn't changed my seat and insulted him. But I was also sorry I had lied to him when he'd asked me if I had been to Zirahúen. I said it was pretty. And from what I had read, Zirahúen was supposed to be an idyllic place. Now I knew I'd have to go there and see for myself.

I had moved up to the front of the bus after the drunken man had gotten off. There was a certain street corner I was looking for...the intersection where I always waited and hailed buses, rather than walking the extra half-mile to the terminal. It shortened my walk to the plaza.

An Indian woman and her tiny daughter got off the bus a few blocks before my stop. The bus driver said to the little girl: "Como se dice, Arios en Purépechan?" She said something that sounded like, "I-yher." It impressed me that such a young child could converse in two languages. The bus driver said that Purépechan sounded a lot like English. He then asked me where I was from, and when I answered, "South Carolina," he replied: "Ah, Paramaribo?" He had thought I had said Suriname. I was a little surprised that he knew that Paramaribo was Suriname's capital city. How many U.S. citizens would have known this? Or even would have known of Suriname, the former colony of Dutch Guiana, in northern South America.

The next day, I hiked to the summit of El Estribo, the cinder cone that overlooks Lake Pátzcuaro. Some of Pátzcuaro's meanest hovels occupy the dirt and cobblestone streets near the road to El Estribo. Tiny, dark children kicked around a soccer ball in the dust. The houses were either adobe or just slatted boards. It was hard to tell if some of these were actually dwellings or just piles of discarded lumber. But there was life behind the boards — human sounds, chickens, music, dogs milling about. I trudged past, stealing a glance here and there; indeed, sometimes my paths took me a little closer to Mexicans' private spaces than I was comfortable with. I wanted to see how people lived, but I didn't want to gawk at their poverty either. I wanted to be an explorer, but I didn't want to cause embarrassment or pain. I left my camera in its case. Remarks made about the backyard of my boyhood home in New Jersey by wealthier kids from an adjacent neighborhood still stung more than 30 years later. We had a large vegetable garden and a kennel for our three dogs. There were brush and compost piles, old lumber, tools and lawn mowing machines. Ours was still a country backyard in a community that had become newly sub-urbanized. Children can be especially cruel, but so can adults. I didn't want to hurt anyone in Mexico.

About a third of the way to the top of El Estribo, where the cobble-stone and dirt road begins to steepen, there is a little school, and then a humble shack of boards stood on end and potted plants and clothes drying on the line. The road is shaded by evergreens here. The air is cool and refreshing. The shack occupies an alpine meadow, with a stupendous view of the valley and mountains towards the southeast. Southern expo-sure! Such an idyllic setting! If one had to be poor, this really wouldn't be a bad place to wake up every morning. Altogether, I counted five dogs and three small children in the yard.

It's difficult to describe the dwelling. It's really just an odd collection of pine boards stood upright, although the whole place appears to lean a bit, as if this shack, like everything else clinging precariously to the side of the mountain, is steadily losing its battle with gravity.

Why are we, in the prosperous and materialist United States, so quick to condemn such a house and dismiss it as a shack? There was much to admire about this dwelling. It was functional; it was simple; it was prob-ably paid for; and it was, no doubt, built by its owners. Thoreau (p. 290) reminds us that:

> Most men appear never to have considered what a house is, and are actually though needlessly poor all their lives because they think that they must have such a one as their neighbors have. As if one were to wear any sort of coat which the tailor might cut out for him, or, gradually leaving off palmleaf hat or cap of woodchuck skin, com-plain of hard times because he could not afford to buy him a crown. It is impossible to invent a house still more convenient and luxurious than we have, which yet all would admit that man could not afford to

pay for. Shall we always study to obtain more of these things, and not sometimes to be content with less?

And it occupied a beautiful setting. Indeed, to live in this wonderful place, as a family with three children and five dogs, was to be rich beyond all expectations. And at night, when the sun went down, they could look at all those lights below, and pity those folks living at such close quarters in the city of Pátzcuaro. Here, they were Kings of the mountain; they were a family to be envied.

Off to the southwest, a lone man plowed a small field with a team of two horses. It was a timeless scene — mid-morning, a single deciduous tree standing in the center of the field. The campesino even had on a sombrero. And from where I stood beneath a canopy of cedar trees, I could just barely hear the steel blade slicing through the dry sod. I liked what I saw. It was a pleasant country scene, as if this world were an idyllic place, where men worked at their own pace, according to their own whims, and life went on as it had for centuries. No stress, just honest labor and fulfillment. In reality, I knew nothing about this man or his life other than what this idyllic image allowed me. His life might have been too boring for words; and, like everything else clinging to the side of this cinder cone, he was probably just trying to hang on. But at that very moment, with the sun burning off the morning chill, and the scent of cedar all around me, all I could do was smile.

I met two boys at the top of the mountain — Raul and his sidekick, Alejandro — both, age nine. Raul was the more outgoing of the two, but I couldn't understand everything he said. He told me he was learning some English in school. "Some" English — at last I had found someone whose English was worse than my Spanish. Raul had two sisters, a dog, and many relatives in Morelia. He had never been to the United States, but hoped to go there some day. He liked sports, and he liked to go to the movies. I didn't learn anything about Alejandro, but Raul seemed delighted to talk non-stop. I had the boys stand with their backs toward Lake Pátzcuaro so I could take their picture. They probably thought this was silly, but several weeks later, when I had gotten my film developed, I realized how much I missed this moment and the boys themselves. I wondered if I would ever see them again, and felt a little sad when I realized I probably never would. But on this morning, Raul's chatter had tired me, and when we had gotten back down to the outskirts of Pátzcuaro, I gave them some pesos so they could get some sodas, and we parted company.

The climb up El Estribo, with its changing views along the way, really gives you a good look at the landscape of the Valley of Pátzcuaro. Still, the view is misleading; it's hard to tell how much deforestation has occurred because the volcanic mountains are still mostly pine-covered. The valley bottoms in winter are mostly brown fields, some covered with black ash from recent burning. The fields are small, divided by rock or wire fences. There are horses and cattle and small adobe dwellings. You can see the road that winds around the lake; you can also see small villages with churches and clusters of houses. You can even see the launches motoring to and from the island of Janitzio, a densely populated cinder cone rising from the middle of Lake Pátzcuaro.

My legs ached a little on the walk back down the mountain. Between my morning runs of about eight miles, and my afternoon hikes, I was getting plenty of exercise. Still, I hardly slept. My room at the Posada de San Rafael had no television or phone. The bed was hard and lumpy, the furniture — solid pine and massive — looked hand-made, but the room was dark and cold. There were heavy wooden shutters, and when they were pulled closed and the lights turned out, the room went black. It was too dark, so I began leaving the bathroom light on. It should have been the perfect room in which to sleep soundly, especially at the end of another exhausting day, but that may have been my problem — I was overtired. I stayed tired, from the altitude, the constant travel, from the unfamiliarity of my surroundings. I was also anxious. I was in my forties. I was trying to accomplish something in my career, but I had lost my way. Mexico had humbled me. I had many self-doubts. Was I really seeing this landscape clearly? Was I comprehending what I saw? There were moments when I wasn't absolutely certain what I was doing on this Mexican odyssey or with my career for that matter, and it all bothered me, as though I were failing at my vocation. Maybe I was. But for me, geography has always been more about exploration and discovery than about solving problems. For me, curiosity has always taken precedence over methodology. Perhaps I was coming to the realization that I was simply an observer, a witness, and a writer, rather than a scholar.

Most of the fish restaurants down by the lake were closed. The lake was polluted. Hard times had set in. The few eateries that were open were doing little business when I walked down there the next afternoon. I had decided it was time to go on a boat trip out on the lake. Choking green weeds lined the shore; the water was greenish-brown and most uninviting. I bought a ticket on the embarcero and boarded one of the launches. There was a good crowd of people on this particular boat. It was made of aluminum, was perhaps fifty feet in length, and had benches on both sides of a center aisle. I sat almost across from two teenaged girls, one of whom kept looking at me and smiling, and making me a bit uncomfortable. She couldn't have been more than about eighteen. The launch had a metal canopy to shield us from the sun and rain. A group of middle-aged male musicians were the last people to board, and it wasn't long before we were being serenaded across the water — all for a tip, of course.

As we made our way to the island, I noticed a long, thin water snake race across the surface of the water. I felt a chill go down my spine. I had thought we were too high up at 7,000 feet elevation for water snakes. Was it poisonous?

As we neared the island, a group of Púrepechan fishermen paddled their dugout canoes out to meet us. The launch slowed, as the fishermen demonstrated their delicate butterfly nets. But it was all for show. They weren't really fishing. And as cameras clicked and camcorders whirred, a lone fisherman suddenly broke ranks, paddled over to our launch and held out a plastic bowl in which to solicit "donations." The "fishermen," as well as the musicians, were simply a bunch of beggars.

Everything in Mexico has a price. Even the public restrooms — at the boat landing or in the bus terminals — have an attendant who expects a few pesos before you get to pee. This is how people survive in an economy of underemployment. Mexico must create a million jobs a year just to keep up with the number of young adults entering the work force. Combined unemployment and underemployment account for roughly 40 percent of the labor force.

While some of Janitzio's residents still try to survive by fishing and begging, the south side of the volcanic island is dominated by eateries and crafts shops. The island is essentially a small-scale tourist trap. And, of course, this is the island where the most famous Day of the Dead celebration in all of Mexico is held. According to Howard La Franchi of the *Christian Science Monitor*:

> Every year crowds now fill Pátzcuaro to overflowing on the
> occasion — as we discovered to our crying children's dismay one
> evening when overwhelmed restaurants ran out of food early.
> And the island of Janitzio in adjacent Pátzcuaro — long a traditional
> Day of the Dead pilgrimage site — can almost rival Daytona Beach
> or Texas' South Padre Island in March.

Every November 2, Mexicans spend the night in the cemetery where their ancestors are buried. They light candles to illuminate memorials composed of orange marigolds known as cempasuchitl flowers. It is an ancient tradition blending indigenous religion and Roman Catholicism. Michoacános have complained, however, that rowdy students come from as far away as Mexico City to stage loud, all-night parties, rather than to honor the dead. Mr. La Franchi discovered, however, that if one traveled outside of Pátzcuaro and the island of Janitzio to some of the lesser known villages that the Day of the Dead was still a wonderful experience.

The launch circled the entire island of Janitzio before letting us off. The south side of the island was commercial, but all around the east, north, and west sides were humble residences, where women and girls were busy washing clothes in the lake. On the west side adjacent to the wharves, a middle-aged man stood waist deep in the water, all lathered up with soap. No wonder the lake was green with scum. The phosphates were sucking the life out of it, not to mention the sewage that flowed from the residences.

Nevertheless, at the little eatery at the top of the volcanic island, where I had stopped and rested and drank a cerveza, there must have been 40 or 50 whitefish, eight to ten inches long, lined up on a board awaiting cleaning. The island lived off tourism. It was peppered with little eateries and shops selling wood carvings and pottery and junk we can all live without. But it was also a popular destination for wedding parties, as a large and jovial group of people, all dressed up and coated in confetti, were ascending the steps as I was going down.

I made my way down along the shore where I photographed some of the dugout canoes. And as I turned and headed up the steps back in the direction of the commercial area, I was met by three small children who wanted me to pay them to take their picture. I gave the first small boy a half-peso coin and snapped their photograph. But that wasn't enough! They wanted more. I dug in my pocket and found another half-peso and snapped another picture. But there were three children, and the third, a girl, expected the same. I dug in my pocket once more, but all I had was a five-peso coin. I wasn't going to give her that, so I began to walk away. She whined! She pleaded with me! She tugged at my shirt. She became angry, nasty. Fortunately, I couldn't understand all that she said. Her anger saddened me. I had seen all I wanted of this little tourist trap. I made my way back to the launches.

The lake became choppy. The pilot of the launch unrolled a large cloth tarpaulin to cover the windows and keep the spray from washing over us. Some of the passengers then decided to tip the pilot. He smiled graciously and thanked them for the tip. He was as shameless as the fishermen, the musicians, and the little girl who had begged and tugged at my sleeve.

There was trash all along the road connecting the perimeter highway to the lake. Hundreds of buses, cars, bicycles, and pairs of feet ply this route daily. I bought a cold soda from a brand new vending machine near the train depot. A woman came along lugging two large pails full of whitefish. I had watched her paddling her dugout in towards shore about thirty minutes earlier. She stopped briefly to rest and I looked inside her buckets. The biggest fish was about a foot long. She smiled at me, then hailed an approaching bus. She climbed aboard with her pails of fish and the bus vanished from my view.

I assume this woman was heading into the market to sell her fish. They wouldn't have fetched many pesos. The scale of her operation was so tiny compared to a commercial fisherman in Maine or Massachusetts. So simple, too. I imagined her paddling her canoe back across the lake that afternoon, back home to one of the many Purepéchan villages that line its shore. I imagined her cooking and cleaning and tending to a husband and children. I'm not sure what the future holds for this woman, whether this lifestyle is going to be sustainable given the pollution of the lake. But at the very moment I had gazed into her buckets of fish, she had seemed perfectly content. I could see it in her eyes.

Could it be that we worry far too much about the future in the United States? I've often thought that the happiest people in Maine were the lobster fishermen, clam diggers, and others who got up every morning and accepted what nature had to offer. There's a lot to be said for enjoying the day at hand, rather than always waiting for something in the distant future. Who can predict what's going to happen anyway?

I dropped my empty soda can in a rectangular drain by the train station. It was already overflowing with trash. Except for the plazas of Mexican towns, which contain trash barrels, and which are swept clean every morning, the outskirts of towns and villages are likely to be strewn with litter. But is all this litter really due to a lack of trash receptacles? How much of Mexicans' propensity to litter is cultural? To dwell is to camp; hence, the campsite becomes a midden heap. But Mexicans seem constantly to be in motion. Mexican life is a continuous street market of vendors, eaters, nibblers, sippers, and consequently, trash generators. Perhaps the need to eat on the move also stems from poverty. How many of these people sucking on oranges and sodas are homeless or in transit? Michoacán is a poor state. People are always coming and going. The evidence collects in the drains, ditches, and along the roadsides.

By mistake, I chose the longer of the two routes up from the lake to get back to town. I passed some shops where they were making furniture, then entered one of Pátzcuaro's least desirable areas. The road crossed a small mountain stream before veering west, and here I stopped dead in my tracks. It was the overpowering stench; also the sight of the garbage —

mounds of it — filling the stream and its banks, which came within a few feet of tiny brick and mortar houses occupied by families with children. I leaned on the railing of the bridge and looked down in horror at the squalor. Then I heard little squeaks. The garbage was alive. The bits and pieces of soiled paper and cardboard were moving. There were small dark images moving daintily amongst the refuse.

At first, I saw just one. Is that a rat? I looked hard at the rotting heaps; the garbage really was moving. It was a fat one, too. And then I saw another, and another, until, to my horror, I realized that the whole streambed was teeming with rats.

A young man was also leaning over the concrete bridge. He just stood there silently, transfixed by what he saw...moving amid the mounds of wet paper boiling up in the fetid stream. The houses on the stream bank were adobe, or brick and mortar, with corrugated roofs. The dwellings seemed to hang precariously on ledges just above the rat-infested stream. I could hear the voices of women and children inside. Wouldn't they be bothered by the stench? Weren't they afraid of diseases, of rat bites in the night? I couldn't bear to look. Yet, I couldn't stop looking. It was appallingly wretched. How could they stay in those houses? Why didn't they go somewhere, anywhere, away from these vermin? First, I saw only the one rat. Then my eyes adjusted to the images. I quickly counted six more. But there were many others. It seemed like all the trash was in motion — a movable feast. The stench was rising. I feared I'd get ill just from breathing it in. And as I began to move away, a boy of perhaps twelve or thirteen arrived with an air rifle — a simple BB-gun, the kind I used as a boy growing up in New Jersey, to shoot at blue jays who came to feast on our Queen Anne Cherries. The boy began to take aim at the fat bellies of the rodents. I had seen enough.

But this was a side of Pátzcuaro I had never before seen. Pátzcuaro, my favorite Mexican town; I had always thought of it as a mountain paradise. I began to see it more clearly — the crumbling colonial landscape, the tacky crafts shops, the polluted lake, the commercialized Day of the Dead and the culture of greed it had spawned among the pathetic fishermen, musicians, entrepreneurs, and opportunists, for which there is no escape except maybe emigration to the United States. All around Pátzcuaro could be heard the chopping, pounding, and sawing of the wood carvers and furniture makers, hacking away at the dwindling stands of pine...to make tens of thousands of worthless trinkets to sell to tourists like me. But how many wooden birds and masks and statues of St. Francis can you carry in your knapsack or put on your mantle at home? Pátzcuaro is a sad testimonial to the axiom that you cannot run an economy on handicrafts. On the contrary, you ultimately create a remittance economy, where the best and the brightest are expected to seek their fortunes elsewhere. One that eerily reminded me of Downeast Maine, with its influx of craftspeople, and its continued outmigration of natives.

When I first visited Pátzcuaro in 1991, I was so impressed by the woodworking that I wrote in my notebook: Pátzcuaro smells like eucalyptus and pine! Some of the old churches have wooden floors — thick planks, four hundred years old, or else squares and triangles of oiled and polished pine. I've never seen so many woodcarving shops — or so many woodcarvers, laboring away with mallets and chisels — where you can purchase life-sized carvings of Jesus or St. Francis, birds, ducks, and other creatures, masks, bowls, beds, chests, desks, doors, and window boxes.

I learned that the Mexican government does not permit any changes to the facades of buildings in Pátzcuaro. The town is indeed a monument to the colonial past — a Mexican Williamsburg or Sturbridge — but without as many tourists, except of course, on the Day of the Dead. A Spanish bishop named Vasco de Quiroga had arrived here in 1540 to reconstruct Pátzcuaro after it had been ravaged by Nuño de Guzman, an infamous conquistador who had tortured and murdered the Indians who had refused to disclose the whereabouts of gold deposits. When Quiroga arrived, he encouraged each Indian village around Lake Pátzcuaro to establish its own craft specialty. Today, Pátzcuaro boasts the Casa de las Artesanias de Michoacán, a house of crafts situated in a former convent, where local craftsmen make and sell ceramics, clothing and textiles, copperwork, jewelry, lacquered wood, musical instruments, paintings, woodcarvings and furniture.

A little motorized train transported children around the plaza on Sunday evening. A man riding a lawn tractor served as the train's engineer. I watched the goings-on from my table inside the El Patio Restaurant, which was nearly empty on this February night. This was not Yucatán or the perpetual springtime of Cuernavaca. This was winter in highland Mexico. I might have been the only tourist in Pátzcuaro this frigid night. I might also have been witness to the slow death of a town that has only tourism to live by.

By nine o'clock the streets were nearly empty. The little train had vanished from the plaza. All the families and children had gone home. A solitary man weaved through the nearly deserted plaza holding a half-empty bottle of Don Pedro Brandy by the neck. Most of the shops had closed. The air smelled of wood smoke. It was cozy. I wouldn't have wanted to be anywhere else but home.

There's something wonderful, but at the same time, extremely sad about Pátzcuaro. Perhaps, in a nutshell, it is symptomatic of the whole country — it seems to hang by a thread, living from day to day, often seeming hopeless. So much idleness; so many days just like the day before — what I had taken for colonial quaintness, I was now seeing as a form of retardation, of wasted lives, and unfulfilled expectations. No wonder the young woman who had fled an abusive and possessive boyfriend in Los Angeles was bored here. Pátzcuaro might have had a colorful past, but what was its future, or hers, for that matter?

And in my ice cold hotel room that evening, I thought: If I ever had to live in Mexico (and I had been there long enough at that point to almost feel like it was destined to be my home...and that I'd never be able to leave), I would choose to live in Mexico City! As much as I claim to despise cities...towards the end of my journey, I had begun to see the country the way so many Mexicans see it — as a hollow shell, a veneer, with nothing below the surface. The civilization, modernization, and liv- ability seem only to be skin deep. Indeed, why do so many Mexicans want to live in Los Angeles, Atlanta, Denver, Dallas, or Chicago? They know. They know there's nothing here: old crumbling churches, Pre- Columbian ruins, crafts made for tourists, eroded and ruined agricultural landscapes, choice lands owned by the privileged few, superficial and overpriced beach resorts staffed by underpaid Mexicans but built for wealthy foreigners — you cannot provide a decent standard of living from any of the above. Average Mexicans have litter, squalor, noise, pollution, bad television, low wages, underemployment, and second-class buses. Only Mexico City has real layers of culture, a sizable middle class, real excitement and variety. It is the classic primate city, overshadowing every other provincial capital. By this point in my journey, I had visited more than 15 cities, many of them considered among the most attractive and interesting in the country. But once you get beyond the colonial architec- ture, the market, and the museums, you realize that the opportunities are limited. For a city to really flourish it has to offer hope and opportunity for upward mobility. In the majority of these provincial towns, expecta- tions are predetermined from birth into a certain social class.

From my base in Pátzcuaro, I visited a variety of settlements in the area, including Erongaricuaro, Pichátaro, Santa Clara del Cobre, Tacámbaro, and Ario de Rosales. All of these towns except Santa Clara del Cobre were first examined by the geographer Dan Stanislawski fifty years earlier (Stanislawski, 1950). And with the exception of Santa Clara, which makes copper products for tourists, the remaining places appeared to have changed little in the last half-century.

Tacámbaro, which is about an hour's bus ride south of Pátzcuaro, occupies an attractive mountain setting. It perches on the steep sides of the volcanic plateau; the Pacific coastal ranges loom majestically off to the south. I had waited in Pátzcuaro's bus terminal for at least an hour, studying the names of the bus lines — Paraiso, Fletcha Amarilla, Transportes de Occidente, Galeana, Enlaces Terrestres Nacionales (ETN), Herradura de Plata — when finally, the call came for the little minibus to Tacámbaro. I was impressed with the young men who hollered out the arrivals and departures, then climbed aboard and rode shotgun on these second-class buses. They must surely possess some of the most powerful vocal chords in Mexico. You can hear them clearly above the roar of the engines as they repeat their destinations in rapid-fire succession: "Oo-rap-pan, Oo-rap-pan, Oo-rap-pan (Uruapan); Arioh! Arioh! Arioh! (Ario de Rosales); Pee-shátaro-Shee-ran! Pee-shátaro-Sheeran! (Pichátaro and Cherán); Tac-cám-baro! Tac-cám-baro! Tac-cám-baro! (Tacámbaro). Once underway, they sell tickets and make change for everyone who boards en route. It doesn't seem like a bad job; and for a teenager, it might even be glamorous; to always be on the move, and in the small societies of Pátzcuaro or Tacámbaro, to be part of the "crew." But imagine making the same run every day, several times a day. Imagine the fumes, the broken mufflers, the worn-out shock absorbers, the stench of body odor, the sickeningly sweet smell of food, and the squawking and squealing and squirming of grimy children. These agile young men learn to move back and forth down the aisles with ease, squeezing between the standing passengers while the bus jounces along, all the while holding the big wad of paper bills folded by denominations in just a certain way — between their fingers — as they use their thumb and index finger to tear off a receipt from a booklet held in the other hand. It appears awkward, even chaotic; in reality, every passenger is accounted for, every peso meticulously collected. I can honestly say that I do not believe I have ever been overcharged or given incorrect change on one of these buses. In its own way, the Mexican bus system works marvelously, transporting people to and from their destinations quickly and efficiently, with a minimum of inconvenience. There is nothing comparable to it in the United States or Canada. Mexico may have its polluted streams, its hillside slums, and its litter-strewn roads; but those roadways are relatively free of traffic, except for these buses, which are getting the masses to their destinations with considerably less fossil fuel than we burn in the U.S. with our 200 million private automobiles. Moreover, the Mexicans are putting far less carbon dioxide into the earth's atmosphere.

The bus to Tacámbaro carried us through pine-covered mountains, past little villages of wooden plank houses with corrugated roofs. The minibus eventually filled to standing-room only — teenaged Indian girls, old women, working men, young boys, even a couple of crates of roosters. It was a perfect bus ride on a perfectly sparkling winter day in the middle of nowhere. Sometimes you experience these fleeting moments in your life; they're not tangible, there's nothing substantive to mark your passage, but you feel this warmth, this sunny glow, this inner peace. We rounded a bend at one point, and down in the valley was a tiny shimmering lake — the sun's rays splayed across its surface at their low, winter angle — nestled against a background of dark green pines casting shadows on the golden landscape. I'll never forget that scene; just like I'll never forget my first images of Sevina or Chalma, fleeting glances of seemingly idyllic places that when, or if ever revisited, could never be as perfect as that one brief glimpse gotten from the window of the second-class bus.

In Tacámbaro, I saw a young man walking down the middle of a sun-splashed street carrying a whole side of bloody beef upon his bare shoulders. He wore a tank top. The mutilated cow still had its tail.

Sometimes you see things in Michoacán that steal your appetite. Once, while crossing a street adjacent to the small, market plaza in Pátzcuaro, I saw a man suddenly jump out the door of a city bus as it rolled to a stop. And as his feet hit the pavement, a shower of orange-colored vomit came spewing out of his mouth. I turned my head away quickly, only to come face to face with the severed head of a cow, completely devoid of skin, as it was being transported down the street in a wheelbarrow. I turned my head back the other way and saw the man braced up against the side of the bus. He steadied himself with both hands, retched, then proceeded to puke his guts out. In a minute he was finished; he climbed back on board, and the bus pulled away, leaving behind a big orange puddle.

Bright red bougainvillea and tall, purple jacaranda trees festooned Tacámbaro's pretty plaza. The sidewalk on the north side was considerably higher than on the south as the town is built into the escarpment. Walking the blocks uphill towards the perimeter road encircling the northern side of town, you eventually come to a point where you have to stop and look straight up; there, perched above you as you crane your neck, are more small houses, resting precariously on the ledges. When approaching the city on the winding perimeter road, you look down and see hundreds of red-tiled roofs, and of course, the cathedral on the plaza. Tacámbaro has all the mysterious mountain beauty of Pátzcuaro, but without the craft shops and tourist hotels. There were some hotels here, but I wasn't sure what I'd be in for, so I decided to make it a day trip. I might have missed something. Tacámbaro, Uruapan, and Ario de Rosales are typical of those settlements which develop on sites that lie on the boundaries of landform regions; in his case, where the volcanic mountains drop down to the hot plains of the Rio Balsas River. They occupy sites that geographers call break-in-bulk; meaning, that cargo often has to be transferred from one mode of transport (river) to another (wheeled vehicle).

Indeed, it is here at the break-in-bulk site that products such as citrus and rice from the hot lands are traded for apples and cherries and strawberries from the volcanic highlands. These are busy towns, with bustling markets selling limes, lemons, plums, potatoes, apples, bananas, and oranges; yet everything looks tiny. Not the big, beautiful produce grown on large farms in the Bajio of Guanajuato and then shipped to companies like Birds Eye in the United States: here was the produce the campesinos ate — tiny potatoes, no bigger than golf balls; tiny fishes perhaps four inches in length, split wide open exposing a sea of bones; miniature bananas that you could eat by the half-dozen.

I walked the steep streets of Tacámbaro in the mid-day sun, dodging big, brown wasps that seemed to be coming at me from all directions. I didn't linger. I'm allergic to wasp stings. The minibus to Pátzcuaro was filling up, so I bought a ticket and a Coke at the tiny Transportes de Occidente office and climbed aboard.

Erongaricuaro and Pichátaro are smaller and more Purépechan than Tacámbaro or Ario de Rosales, which are primarily mestizo, and which resemble each other in size, location, and function. Erongaricuaro is a village on the western edge of Lake Pátzcuaro, while Pichátaro is an Indian village on the road to Cherán. Both towns are good places to buy pine furniture; in fact, while I was walking the streets of Pichátaro, a young man approached me and asked if I had come there to buy furniture. Even though I hadn't, he led me inside a compound where his grandfather — a very old man — was carving a wooden frame for a large wall mirror. Everything about the compound was Purépechan — the plank house of heavy timbers, hip roof, and wide eaves; the ears of corn drying from the porch overhang; the lazy street dogs (I counted nine); and the Indian women by the well, doing their laundry, stealing glances at me, and giggling shyly. It wasn't until the sound of Frank Sinatra singing My Way came blasting from a stereo near the little zócalo that I was suddenly jolted back to the western world. Pichátaro was an agricultural settlement, but the town exported furniture to the United States. The young man who introduced me to his grandfather also had many parientes (relatives) in California. I walked around the village for a while, admiring the fruit trees, the many traditional plank houses of various ages and states of disrepair, and began wondering what it would be like to live in one. The town had few cars and trucks; some of the men and boys were riding horses; and on the outskirts, a man plowed a field with oxen. It was higher in elevation than Pátzcuaro, and when the wind gusted it was quite chilly. I tried to stay in the sun. At one point I was greeted by two very drunk old men. They detained me in the middle of the street for a few minutes, asking me a barrage of questions, none of which I could understand well enough to answer. Their teeth were rotten or missing; they stank of sweat and bad breath. I just told them I was a professor of geography, that I was traveling through Mexico to see what the land and people were like. I told them I thought it was very pretty there. They eventually became bored with me and moved down the street.

I had to get out of this place but I also had to go to the bathroom. The town only had one tiny eatery that doubled as a video store, but they wouldn't let me use the bathroom. It was evidently in someone's house. I began inquiring around for a public restroom. At last, a young man led me through a wooden gate at the rear of the town health clinic and directed me to a lone lean-to of boards standing in a field. It was a primitive outhouse. I knocked my hat off as I pulled aside the heavy canvas that served as a door and ducked inside. All this time, I knew I was being watched. Three young men, who had been working on the roof of a new cement-block house nearby, were suddenly waving, smiling, then laughing heartily, as I emerged smiling and anxious to return their gestures of friendship...all this, as if to suggest that I, a gringo, surely was not accustomed to such primitive plumbing. If only they knew. If only they could see our outhouse behind the camp in Maine! If they only knew we had no electricity or facilities of any kind. They might be surprised that Linda and I have been living that way in the summertime since we were married in 1975. She says she enjoys the change from the other nine months; although she's always ready to get back to the modern conveniences each fall. I can't speak for Linda, but I'm one of those eccentrics who still believes Thoreau was right. I've embraced the notion of voluntary simplicity. The teaching job, the house in South Carolina, these are the concessions that must be made the other nine months in order to pay the bills and keep the marriage together. Where would I be without the responsibilities and structure of marriage? A clamdigger passing the winter in that cabin on the pond?

At last, it was time to visit Zirahuén, the village along the shore of a sparkling blue lake nestled between the pine-covered mountains. This was the town that the drunk I had met on the bus from Quioga had said he was from. I rode there on an ancient school bus with torn seats that had been taped over, and cracked glass in most of its windows. Religious paraphernalia hung from the rearview mirror, perhaps offering some comfort to the hapless driver and his motley assortment of passengers as it wheezed and whined over the mountains into Zirahuén.

There were lots of horses here. It appeared as if Zirahuén had not yet made the transition to the automobile era. It was quiet. No drunks found me, or I them. There was a collection of open-air fish restaurants by the lake shore, where a path led to two outdoor privies — HOMBRES Y MUJERES. The bus that had discharged me had gone on to another village called Agua Verde (Green Water), so I was stranded here, some five kilometers over the mountains from the main highway back to Pátzcuaro.

A few couples were arriving by taxi this afternoon, perhaps to enjoy a quiet fish dinner and a couple of drinks. There were two little kiosks where you could buy a piña colada. Zirahuén had a much smaller, less festive launch area than Lake Pátzcuaro. The water looked cleaner as well...cleaner, but not clean. Compared to lakes and ponds in Maine, the water looked muddy. A sailboat shimmered off in the distance. Three teenaged girls toting guitars boarded a large covered launch at the dock. Perhaps there was going to be a wedding or a party.

The town of Zirahuén isn't much — some dirt streets, some interesting old wooden buildings with wide eaves. I was especially drawn to the woodwork inside the church. It was a substantial, rectangular structure with a high ceiling made of wide pine boards. It had an inviting light, as if His presence was reassured, and a warmth uncharacteristic of the stone and masonry churches elsewhere in the republic. It would have been easy to come here on a daily basis, to kneel and pray, and sit and meditate amidst the warm, soothing glow. Really...it wasn't a bad place to wind up.

After more than a decade of traveling the backwaters of the Mexican heartland, I felt as if I had come to the end of the road. The drunk had lured me to his village and now I was stranded here. There were only the sounds of nature...the incessant buzzing of big, brown wasps, hundreds, maybe thousands of them, flitting about. It was only a matter of time. I couldn't dodge them forever. I am severely allergic to wasp stings! But I carried nothing...no medication of any kind. I had some Benedryl in my knapsack, but it was back at the hotel in Pátzcuaro. And the only way out of here was to walk...over the mountains, in the heat of the day. So onward I marched, into the clouds of buzzing insects, as the tropical sun burned my ears, neck, and face. The wasps seemed to swarm closer! I was a goner! GEOGRAPHY PROFESSOR DEVOURED BY MEXICAN MAN-EATING WASPS.

Evidently, it wasn't my time. A little Datsun taxi came chugging up the hill. I flagged him down. I was relieved, but also a little disappointed to see him. I was enjoying this solitary odyssey. A few minutes later, the driver discharged me and his other passenger, a tiny old woman, at the intersection of the highway back to Pátzcuaro.

Heavily armed soldiers manned a roadblock at the highway intersection, where they stopped every vehicle and searched its trunk. I asked the old woman if it was drugs they were looking for. "Si! Si! Las drogas!" she growled. "It's a big problem." Indeed! A middle-aged man I had met in the plaza in Pátzcuaro had identified three problems that were affecting Michoacán: "Number one, the PRI lost here in 1988 and they haven't put much money into the state. This is a Cardenas stronghold (PRD-center-left-party). Number two, tourists have been getting held up by banditos along the highways. This is scaring people away. And three, the drugs. They're growing marijuana in the hills around here. This state is the next Chiapas."

He told me all this in a grave voice. He sold building supplies for a living. His business was faltering. He never cracked a smile during our entire conversation. Sadness and resignation were written all over his face.

"Are there guerrillas here?" I had asked him.

"No. But things are very bad. This is one of the poorest states. We don't want another revolution like 1910, but things have to change."

I hadn't encountered many tourists — a few elderly, the usual assortment of Brits, Germans, and Canadians. It seemed like each year I came to Pátzcuaro it was deader than the year before. The tourist trade seemed to be drying up. Most of the fish restaurants down by the lake were closed.

Meanwhile, back at the highway intersection...the old woman couldn't have been much taller than four-feet-eight, but she was as tough as Tugboat Annie. The soldiers and their machine guns didn't intimidate her. She brushed right by them, strode out into the middle of the highway and hailed us a bus. Once on board, she went right to sleep.

Seeing how quickly the old woman had passed into sleep, I began to wonder about the elderly here. All these tiny, shrunken women, toting their nylon sacks on and off the buses and up and down the dusty streets: What do these women worry about? Do they worry about money the way young people do? Or do they reach an age when they no longer worry about worldly problems and simply put their trust in God? What is it like to grow old and toothless and wrinkled in this culture? Mexicans are said to be fatalistic. Gringos live to work; Mexicans work to live. Today is what matters. Perhaps God takes care of tomorrow. Such a contrast from the United States where we've become obsessed with preparing for retirement. From the time we are in our early thirties we hear: Are you putting enough money away? How diverse is your portfolio? Your medical expenses during the final year of your life could be as high as those of your entire life! Will you have enough money to be comfortable in retirement, to maintain your current lifestyle? Seeing these old women — who usually appeared happy and content — I began to wonder about the way we view aging, the elderly, and retirement in the United States.

I also wondered how my own mother, who is 85 and has never had any desire to visit Mexico, would react to this place. What would she think of these women's lives? Would she see the beauty, the spirituality, the warmth in their faces? Or would she see only the poverty, the hard lives they must endure?

Nearly everything in Pátzcuaro begins to look worn and dirty after a while. Part of it was the dry season, the whirling clouds of dust; part of it was my mood, so fickle, so sensitive to my changing surroundings, so somber at times from sleep deprivation. Still, this is a sad place, perhaps an appropriate setting in which to celebrate the dead. Mexico no longer frightened me so much as it saddened me. Wherever I looked on this particular day, I saw those tiny, shriveled-up old women, hauling their bundles up Pátzcuaro's dusty streets on their short spindly legs. This was their lot in life. This was all they'd ever know.

I passed a most fascinating, yet hideously ugly house built atop the noise and fumes and black grease of an automobile repair garage. I was on my way back to town from the lake when I encountered this strange structure. It was three stories, made of cement blocks and painted in a gaudy pink, with tiny rectangular steel-framed windows with dirty screens that gave it the appearance of a hot, airless bunker.

But on top of the house's flat roof was an extensive garden of flowering shrubs, a sort of folksy-leafy arboretum — rare beauty on top of utter decay. I wanted desperately to photograph this unusual dwelling. I discreetly removed by camera from its case and began to position myself for a series of shots.

Then I saw her! She looked like an angel...or, an apparition. A beautiful young woman moved about, in a long, flowing sleeveless dress, tending her flowers. Suddenly the girl noticed me staring up at her! And for an uneasy moment our eyes locked. Meanwhile, in the garage and out on the street below, were several men, some working on cars, others just standing around, loitering and gossiping the way men do. At that moment, I suddenly felt self-conscious. What right did I have to exploit this scene? What if I embarrassed this woman or annoyed the men on the street? Maybe she wouldn't have been embarrassed; maybe she would have smiled and waved. But I didn't want to cause her any pain. It was painful enough just to see her up there...to realize she was a real human being, and this was her home, her own little private world. She had brought color and beauty, and especially dignity, to this dreadful house and street. I put away my camera and quietly moved down the road...then I stopped, turned my head, and stole one more glance.

2000

25

WHEN GLOBALIZATION STRIKES HOME

It is hard to tell from the sheer numbers of brand new sport utility vehicles that unemployment in this South Carolina county is approaching 15 percent. The big, luxury models are everywhere. Aren't they rather expensive, those gas-guzzling behemoths, those symbols of conspicuous consumption? Indeed. Yet parking lots here often seem cavernlike, as if one were wending one's way between the skyscrapers of Manhattan.

People in rural South Carolina have money! Or at least they can get their hands on money, or credit. Those smartly dressed Southern belles seem to be talking constantly — even at eight o'clock in the morning — on their cell phones, while cruising in their Explorers, Expeditions, Excursions, Escalades, Navigators, Tahoes and Suburbans. Hardly anyone in this South Carolina county seems to give a rip about fuel economy anymore. That's old stuff, 1970s talk. Minivans, subcompacts, small cars...they must be for the marginal, the poor, the down and out. High school students here even drive big SUVs. Status has always meant a lot in the rural South. It never ceases to amaze me. Meanwhile, my Southern friends can't seem to understand why I refuse to buy a new car, or make a car payment. "It's just a car!" I say. "Who cares?" But I also have vivid memories of the 1970s, when gas prices soared and the jobs I was lucky enough to get barely paid a living wage.

The most recent plant to close was RAYTEX — more than 200 jobs. The axe came without any warning two weeks before Christmas. Some of those folks had worked at that plant for 30 years! In April, the Russell Stover Candies plant shut its doors, tossing more than 800 people, mostly women, out of work. Between April and December 2000, Marion County, South Carolina, lost another 1,000 jobs, mostly in textiles and apparel.

Abandoned factories line the highways. All sorts of items — fabrics, shirts, towels — that were once made in Maine, Massachusetts and New Hampshire, were made here in rural South Carolina the past 30 years. Not anymore. They're increasingly manufactured in peripheral regions such as Mexico, Central America and the Caribbean. Factory jobs that pay little more than minimum wage here are being "outsourced" to areas of cheaper labor.

"It's the difference between paying $10 an hour and a dollar an hour (including benefits)." That's how my neighbor explained it. He's been here nine years. He came from Missouri. He manages the sole surviving

Sara Lee Hosiery plant. There were five Sara Lee plants in the area when he arrived. All the big decisions are made by corporate executives in New York City. So my neighbor now flies back and forth between South Carolina, New York and Central America, as Sara Lee has recently opened plants in El Salvador, Guatemala, Honduras and Nicaragua. "We looked at Mexico, but it's hard to do business there...too many regulations. And the labor's expensive...more than a dollar an hour." My neighbor didn't tell me what the hourly wage was in Central America, but when I asked him if it was more than a dollar an hour, he said, "Oh, it's not that much!" A couple of years ago, *The Christian Science Monitor* reported that the average factory wage in El Salvador was 56 cents an hour. An article in *Focus* (winter 1997) reported that average hourly wages in Caribbean states varied from 50 cents an hour in the Dominican Republic to as high as $1.25 in Antigua and Barbuda. Of course, 56 cents is still much better than the two dollars a day an average rural Dominican or Salvadoran earns.

Ain't globalization great? What a world we've created at the beginning of the 21st century, where the rich seem to be getting much richer, the poor in a handful of developing countries are slightly better off, and the middle and working classes, especially in industrial countries like the United States, are simply tossed out of work. Just a few bucks severance pay...that's it. And it doesn't matter whether we've got a Democratic or Republican administration in Washington, global capitalism marches on in search of ever-greater profits, leaving behind a human geography of uneven development. In the 1970s, thousands of people lost their jobs in the "Rust Belt" states of the Midwest; now it's happening in the South.

Many of those who have lost their jobs here in Marion County are black. But not all. Some are white, middle class, and college educated. There's a multiplier effect, where one manufacturing job creates a need for two or three jobs in the service sector. When the plants close there's a ripple effect, where retail stores, restaurants and car dealerships gradually go out of business. Some lucky people take early retirement. Others move away. Some commute long distances. The job losses cut across racial, educational, age and class lines. Globalization is bringing pain to all classes, even if among the privileged the pain is just guilt.

Many of those here in Marion County who are better off work in nearby Florence County, which is crossed by I-95, or else they commute to Myrtle Beach, which is less than 50 miles away. Both of those places are booming. Unemployment is less than 3 percent in Florence County, and Myrtle Beach can't find enough workers. DuPont, General Electric, Hoffman-LaRoche, Honda, McLeod Regional Health Center, Stone

Container and Blue Cross-Blue Shield are some of the largest employers in Florence County. Blue Cross-Blue Shield is the biggest — a giant post-industrial sweatshop, where nearly a thousand workers, women, mostly, sit in front of computer terminals all day, processing insurance claims. (Blue Cross-Blue Shield announced massive layoffs to begin in Florence during the summer of 2004).

Those who commute to Myrtle Beach are part of another 21st century economy — the "leisure-opolis." Myrtle Beach now boasts 100 golf courses, with more on the way. A hundred golf courses! Think about it! And of course there's Planet Hollywood and the NASCAR Cafe, and all the other hotels, restaurants and amusements for tourists. Myrtle Beach is considered to be a paradise for all ages...hedonism run rampant.

Meanwhile, here in Marion County, the local politicians tell folks not to despair. "We'll get some new industry! Times will get better." Named after Francis Marion, the Swamp Fox, people here have deep roots; they're not gonna just up and leave the way folks do in large metropolitan areas. Many people simply can't leave. They don't have the education or the job skills. Family ties are too strong. Some people have never been anywhere else.

"We've got to keep some production here on the mainland. We need to be able to fill rush orders," my neighbor explained. So for now, Sara Lee will keep its remaining plant in the area open. "We've been busy. And you know, the boat plant across town seems to be doing well, too!" my upbeat neighbor added. "They've been adding people." Yeah, but the boat plant is French-owned. They make fiberglass yachts for resorts in the Caribbean. Tourism economies are always vulnerable to recessions on the mainland. The Caribbean suffered mightily during the lean years of the 1970s. "And the furniture industry is holding its own." Right. But they can't afford to ship the oak and walnut and cherry all the way to factories in Central America. It's just not cost effective. After all, isn't that what it's all about?

When you think about it, it's Economics 101. It's all just money. How to make it. Where to make it. The 21st century really isn't much different than the last century.

2001

26

LOVE AND REHABILITATION AT THE ANIMAL SHELTER

We can judge the heart of a man by his treatment of animals. ——
Immanuel Kant

After Hallie, my 16-year-old collie/setter dog, went to heaven, I found myself driving out to the local animal shelter. I needed to be around dogs. I was grieving, and visiting these gentle, abandoned animals brought me some comfort. I had taken Hallie to the veterinarian for the last time, and stroked her soft head while her beloved vet had gently put her to sleep.

It nearly killed me. Nothing in my life, save the untimely death of my father when I was 15, has ever given me such grief. For days, I could scarcely function. I could barely do my job. I kept replaying it in my mind, agonizing over whether I had made the right decision. That sweet, lovable dog was my only child. She, along with my wife, Linda, had always been the center of my world. As long as I had them with me, I could deal with whatever life served up. How fragile we humans are!

The animal shelter, I discovered, was tended by a middle-aged man I'll call Lyle. At first I thought Lyle was a little coarse — an ornery redneck with a twangy, deep woods Southern drawl, who always had a cigarette dangling from his mouth. But as I continued to frequent the shelter, I had many opportunities to observe him with these dogs and cats. He was so good with them. He knew them individually and could tell me about their various temperaments. And the more I spoke with him about the different dogs, the more I came to admire him. These poor abandoned animals had been rescued. They were in good hands. Lyle and I became friends.

It was probably a couple of months before I realized that Lyle was a prisoner. Why hadn't I noticed the stripes running down the legs of his pants? Was I too transfixed on the dogs? Was it simply inconceivable to me that this kind man could have been a convict? I should have figured it out. The animal shelter stood across a large field from the correctional facility.

Eventually, I learned from a friend that Lyle had killed a man. I guess it wasn't premeditated murder, because Lyle was serving a life sentence. Executions are permitted in South Carolina. I never learned all the details, but Lyle was the kindest murderer I've ever known. Well, he was the only murderer I've ever known.

And I wasn't the only one who felt that way. I began to notice that a certain middle-aged woman was spending a lot of time at the animal shelter. This woman, I learned, had been instrumental in getting the shelter established. When we first moved here 15 years ago, Marion County didn't even have an animal shelter. Apparently, this woman, whom I later learned had long ago separated from her husband, saw in Lyle many of the same good qualities I had seen. And it wasn't long before I learned that Lyle and this woman had fallen in love.

Indeed, it seemed like every time I drove out to the shelter, her car was there. She and Lyle now bathed and clipped and dipped and cared for these dogs and cats together.

Rock 'n' roll music sounded from a radio inside the shelter, and you could hear the two of them talking softly as they worked. Lyle, it turned out, was a gifted man. One day, he was even building an oak planter "for the boss lady's garden." He was a hard worker, and meticulous.

Then one day I arrived to find two new prisoners tending the shelter. Two men were now required to do the work that Lyle had done. And when I asked where Lyle was, I was told that he'd been sent away, to another prison more than 100 miles from here. The victim's family had complained that Lyle had too much freedom. No doubt they had also heard about the new woman in his life, who was now driving clear across the state just to be with him on weekends.

And I wondered, as I watched the new prisoners go about their rounds, what had led Lyle to commit murder in the first place. Maybe he hadn't always been so kind and gentle. Perhaps the responsibility of caring for a shelter full of abandoned dogs and cats had softened, tamed and rehabilitated this man, who at some point in his troubled past had snapped and made a terrible mistake.

After ordering the euthanasia of Hallie — no matter how well intentioned it might have been — I eventually realized that the only way I was ever going to heal was to get another dog. We chose a Border Collie — a breed with its own unique behavior problems — a keeper-of-the-flock, who would herd us and look after us and help us get over the death of Hallie.

"She has Hallie's eyes," a neighbor said, when we first brought Bess home. "Hallie must have sent her to you." And I believe she did. Here was another high energy, high spirited, nearly uncontrollable creature — just like Hallie had been — who was ready for action the moment we made eye contact. Border Collies are intense, highly motivated, often obsessive-compulsive dogs. Like Hallie, whose spirit was never broken and who never really calmed down until she was in her teens, Border Collies are the wrong dogs for most people. They are tenacious, which is what often gets them into trouble. They are bred for work and frequently develop behavior problems if their owners neglect them. They need several hours of task or goal-oriented work or play every single day. Owning a Border Collie is a major commitment. Indeed, the literature on Border Collies suggests they are one of the breeds most likely to end up in animal shelters.

A child runs, the Border Collie circles, barks and scares the child into running faster. The Border Collie becomes more aggressive, possibly nipping or biting the child. The owners, convinced there's something terribly wrong with the dog, take it to the pound. It is easy to understand how these loyal, loving dogs, that want only to work and serve and take care of us, can wind up in shelters. What is not clear is why busy couples with young children get Border Collies in the first place. They're pretty dogs, they're extremely intelligent, and unfortunately, they are increasingly used in television commercials — all the wrong reasons to choose a Border Collie! They're intelligent and often a lot smarter than their owners.

Border Collies are among God's most amazing creatures. A 35-pound Border Collie can move a herd of cattle or round up a flock of sheep. They deserve better than to wind up in animal shelters or in homes where they're not kept busy. Fortunately, there's a unique shelter in Melrose, Florida, called Border Collie Rescue. Their Web site has numerous photographs of beautiful Border Collies that were either abandoned or else turned in to the shelter because of "behavior problems." Several of the most obsessive-compulsive dogs at Border Collie Rescue have been placed in an intensive training course called the Birdstrike Program. Graduates are then assigned to Florida airports, where they chase away flocks of birds that can get sucked into jet engines, possibly causing the planes to crash. According to an FAA study, birds collide with some 2,500 planes a year in the United States, causing millions of dollars of damage. A number of airports in North America are now considering employing Border Collies to chase birds away from runways. Let's face it, all of us — dogs and humans — need to work. It keeps us focused on our commitments; it keeps us from going astray.

Probably the earliest domesticated animals, dogs may be just what many troubled humans need. They give unconditional love. And when I look into Bessie's beautiful, brown trusting eyes, as I once did Hallie's, I'm reminded of the sanctity of life, and the terrible price paid when it is violated. And I wonder in this age of ever increasing barbarity, when so-called "civilized" nations tolerate abortion, patient assisted suicide and capital punishment, if we wouldn't be better off sending our murderers to the dogs. What good can possibly come from executions? We could get many years of good service out of these murderers. Better to put them to work cleaning kennels where, like Lyle, they may be fortunate to receive therapy, love and rehabilitation, compliments of "man's best friend."

2001

27

NEVER BE A TEACHER

As a young man, my fondest dream was to become a geographer. However, while working in the customs office I thought deeply about the matter and concluded it was far too difficult a subject. With some reluctance I then turned to physics as a substitute.
Albert Einstein

"Are you busy?"

Anthony, a 34-year-old African-American student, is standing in the doorway of my office 20 minutes before class. "I can come back later if this is a bad time."

"No. No. Come on in, Anthony. I'm not doing anything important." Notes are spread out across my desk — notes that I probably won't even glance at once class begins. I'm just trying to get myself together. I'm 50 years old, yet I still feel a shiver of anxiety before every class.

Anthony and his wife recently had their first child. The new baby is keeping him up at night. He's working part-time and he's a full-time college student. He's all stressed out. We're having a test later in the week. I try to calm his fears. We go over some of the material. I try to encourage him. I've been working with him all semester. He's a graduating senior, a chemistry major, yet he's waited until his last semester to take Cultural Geography 101. Like so many college students, he's largely ignorant of the world beyond his doorstep and is wary of geography. He's heard all those stories about "Lockyer's class."

I suppose if I could have the perfect job it would be that of a serious scholar or major writer, publishing the latest groundbreaking book; but the sad truth is, I've hardly published anything...barely enough to be awarded tenure and eventually a full professorship at a small, regional university in the South. In 25 years of teaching, I've written three books and a handful of articles. Only one of the books has been published, and none of the articles has appeared in a mainstream scholarly journal. If I had been at a flagship university, I would have been sent packing.

At age 50, I'm suddenly feeling a bit deflated. I'm also feeling a sense of urgency, a need to take stock — to stand back and wonder what, if anything, I've been doing all these years. I've produced practically nothing...and I'm running out of time.

I can offer only one explanation: I have been a teacher. I have taught in seven states, the past 15 years in South Carolina. Have I taught well?

Who can say for certain? All I know is that since age 25 when I completed my master's degree, my life has revolved around preparing for class.

"Never be a teacher!" the writer V.S. Naipaul once said.

"I have the best job in the world!" I once heard Stephen King say on *Good Morning America*. He may indeed have the best job in the world. He's certainly earned it. I admire his ability to tell a story, his productivity, his courage and generosity. But if Stephen King has the best job, I just might have the second best.

I have no regrets. There are no other roads I should have taken. The circuitous paths I've chosen have all seemed right. How did I know? I didn't. I just followed my instincts. I allowed myself to be pulled along by my curiosity and interest in geography. I think I could teach it to an empty room. I'm certain that teachers are primarily motivated by their enthusiasm for their disciplines; whether or not anyone else cares about it may be irrelevant. One of my colleagues who has taught political science for more than 30 years insists he can "talk politics to four walls." Teachers try to inspire. That's possible only if one is passionate about one's subject.

And I don't think it really matters whether one teaches at Harvard or Yale, the local high school or grammar school: We're all in the same boat. We've all got to walk into that classroom and perform one of the hardest, most demanding jobs on earth — educate. We have to inspire all right; we also have to motivate, nurture, evaluate, pass, fail and forgive. We have to forgive our students' bad attitudes, ignorance and shortcomings; but most important, we have to forgive ourselves for our own failings as teachers. Whether we choose to be or not, we are caregivers in ways that specialists can never be...in that we're expected to somehow deal with nearly every sort of physical and social problem imaginable.

Students come with "issues." I've dealt with divorces, breakups, batterings, diseases and death. Sure, there are professional counselors. But if the student is in your class, you may ultimately play a bigger role in their lives than anyone. Teachers deal with anger, aggression, anxiety, depression, fear, insecurity, gender, ethnicity, race, good and sometimes, evil. Never be a teacher...that is, unless you want the most challenging and occasionally the most rewarding job a human being could ask for.

"Why don't you become a teacher?" my father always said. "You could have the whole summer off." I think he wanted me to become a teacher because he wanted to be one himself. My father loved books. He gave me my first reading lessons. He had worked in a General Motors ball-bearing plant for 31 years when he died of a heart attack at age 48. He once took me to the plant when I was 12. The noise! The stress! No wonder he had high blood pressure. No wonder he dreamed of retirement.

I do get a nice long summer vacation. But what have I done these past 25 summers? Mostly, I've prepared for class. I spent two summers writing a doctoral thesis. I wrote those three books, those few articles, but mostly I've read, and studied and developed courses — more than a dozen of them. The fact is, I've never really had a summer off. I've never had a week off. Teaching is a year-round job. Thank goodness! I've never been bored.

Even in midsummer, a month removed and still more than a month away from meeting my first class, I occasionally have anxiety dreams about teaching. And after all these years, I'm still nervous before the first class meeting. I still have problems sleeping on Sunday nights — the whole week of classes lies ahead.

What can I possibly say that will interest these jaded, self-centered, sophisticated college students? I'm going to walk in there tomorrow morning and 40 of them are going to be staring at me! Many of them wear more stylish clothes and drive nicer cars than I; some of them have traveled to more exotic places than I; they come from an electronic and digital culture I can scarcely comprehend; and of course, they're nearly all much younger than I. Yet there I stand — middle-aged and feeling almost naked — trying to explain the Arab-Israeli conflict, ethnic cleansing in the Balkans, the domestication of plants, the trade winds, or the reasons hungry women in war-torn Rwanda still want six or seven babies. Meanwhile, the human and physical geography of the planet grows ever more complex as governments fall, empires disintegrate, boundaries change, and new states are added — 192 countries at last count, not to mention the scores of nationalist movements...Palestine, Kurdistan, Kosovo, etc. I teach four courses a semester to about 120 students. I've got 15 weeks to explain the entire world.

"When are you going to retire?" my old high school classmates often ask. Retire? Retire from what? I teach two classes a day. Mostly I just enjoy myself. "How is Allan going to be able to tell when he's retired?" one of my more savvy friends likes to joke. Like many professors, I spend much of the day reading and shooting the bull with students and colleagues. We love bad news. Oh, yeah, we thrive on it, especially if it involves departmental budgets and salaries. It gives us something to whine and moan about. Campus history often fuels our conversation. Grousing about the evil and ineptitude of past administrations leaves us almost blissful. We love a good story. We especially enjoy a good scandal. We like to share "war" stories about when we had a certain weirdo or a memorable coed in our classes. Oh, sure, we advise students, grade papers, prepare lectures, serve on countless committees, travel, do research, write books and articles, attend conferences, but mostly we enjoy ourselves. What could possibly be more enjoyable than sitting around all day talking about history and geography, politics and economics, or culture and society with friends and colleagues? And I'm getting paid for this! Maybe my father was on to something.

So I'm just delighted when Anthony stops by my office. His presence helps to justify my existence.

"I always heard you were really hard. But your class isn't that bad if you work at it," Anthony says with a smile.

"I thought Chemistry was supposed to be hard, Anthony."

"Shoot. This is the hardest course I've had. I had no idea there was this much to geography. I thought it was just learning places on a map."

Anthony pulls out a dog-eared collection of outline maps that he's scribbled notes and other information across: areas of low and high pressure, prevailing winds, population data, birth and death rates, migration flows, ethnic groups, languages, religions. The course does seem to have opened up a new world for him. He asks me to explain the seasonal shift of the intertropical convergence, then he wants to know what this has to do with Islam and Arab slavery in East Africa.

"The Arabs followed the prevailing trade winds, Anthony. So did Columbus. He could have floated over here on an inner tube."

Then Anthony added, "And the Spanish brought all those diseases that killed off the Indians. So they turned to Africans to work in the mines and on the plantations. I'm beginning to see how it all fits together."

Indeed, it is truly wonderful to sit across from Anthony (an African-American who, 50 years ago when I was born, would not have been able to attend most state universities in the South), one scholar to another and converse calmly and thoughtfully rather than emotionally about highly sensitive racial issues. This is what education can be. It is one of the many reasons I am a teacher.

Anthony wants to be a sales representative for a pharmaceutical company. He's a hot job prospect. In a year or two, he'll probably be earning more money than his professor. His future wasn't always this promising. He dropped out of college in the 1980s. He wound up bagging groceries at a Winn-Dixie supermarket. Eventually he became a manager-trainee. He ended up being the store manager. "I could have stayed there the rest of my life. But it really wasn't what I wanted to do," he explained, almost apologetically. "I had a dream. So I quit my job at Winn-Dixie and came back to school."

I admire Anthony. It takes courage to go back to school at any age.

Women seem to be able to pull it off more frequently than men. Sometimes they have no choice. My mother enrolled in college after my father died. She was 57 when she graduated with a teaching degree from the University of Maine at Machias.

And it was with much trepidation that I gave up a steady teaching job back in 1982 to pursue a doctorate in Colorado. I was 31 at the time, and the job outlook for college professors could not have been bleaker. Undaunted, I remained optimistic that I had chosen the right path. Over the years, students like Anthony have reaffirmed this.

Anthony got an A in Cultural Geography. Believe me, he earned it.

2001

28

ROUTE 7: CENTRAL MAINE'S HIGHWAY TO HEAVEN

I grew up across the road from a small dairy farm in north-central New Jersey. This was an old village. Our house, which my parents moved to from Newark in 1950, was built in 1709. Two large trees shaded the house — a horse chestnut and a honey locust. A soldier from the Revolutionary War was buried beneath the honey locust. He was carried home in a wheelbarrow from the nearby Battle of Springfield. He died on the way. His ghost was said to inhabit the attic of our house.

The dairy farm across the road was owned by a man named George Smith, who still milked his cows by hand. Our next-door neighbor was a minister who also raised laying hens. Four big chicken barns stood in his backyard, which extended all the way back to a large wooded area known as the East Orange Water Reserve. It was here, among those straight rows of planted white pines and surviving stands of hardwood forests, which were peppered with NO TRESPASSING signs, that my quiet, introverted personality took shape. I might have grown up in suburban New Jersey, but I spent much of my childhood as a "fugitive," hiding out in those woods.

Our neighbor on the other side was a pediatrician who raised Arabian horses. In a sense, we were still "country," even though we were less than 20 miles west of Newark.

How quickly places change and agricultural landscapes are transformed! In the late 1950s the bulldozers arrived. Mr. Smith had sold his farm to a developer and had moved his herd to Freehold, a town in south-central New Jersey. Freehold was an agricultural community that later gained notoriety as the home of the "Boss," rock legend Bruce Springsteen.

I couldn't have been much older than 6 or 7 when the bulldozers cleared the land for the "Farmstead" subdivision. And from then until age 15, when my father died and my mother and I moved to Steuben, Maine, in 1966, all I can remember is dramatic and devastating social and environmental change — forests cleared, ponds drained, roads cut and then paved, subdivisions built across the former cow pastures, city people with new cars and new clothes and new furniture moving into brand new houses.

I'm certain I started down the path toward becoming the curmudgeon I am today the moment the bulldozers arrived. I've always despised developers; I've always hated change. As a result, I have chosen to make my homes in backwaters — Marion County, South Carolina, and Gouldsboro, Maine. I'm continually on the lookout for attractive places deeper in the bush where I might someday retreat when the developers arrive.

It was with this idea that I recently drove Route 7, Maine's Moosehead Highway, from Belfast up to Dover-Foxcroft. The economic windfall of MBNA seemed to reach at least 20 miles into the interior of bucolic Waldo County. Most of the homes here — old and new — are attractive and nicely maintained. But the first 10 miles or so of Route 7 north of Belfast is barely passable in places. Poor Maine. Evidently the DOT simply hasn't the funds to maintain this stretch of highway. Which was fine with me! I wanted to creep along at 20 miles an hour and savor this narrow ribbon of ecstasy, which winds its way over hill and dale into the quaint village of Brooks.

Here was an idyllic 19th century crossroads village — white clap-boarded community church, general store, hardware store, big old stately homes with attached barns, and the stream frothing and careening over the rocks. Here was the picture-postcard Maine village to die for! And it wasn't all gunked up and yuppified with incense and candle shops and "country" inns, like those dreadful little coastal villages tourists love.

And it wasn't long before that childhood smell of George Smith's cow pasture permeated my senses — a dairy farm! Somewhere along that narrow, winding country lane, a working dairy farm appeared on the left. I can't remember which town it was in — Brooks? Jackson Corners? Dixmont? North Dixmont? I was too dazzled by the beauty and serenity of the landscape. Every dwelling — prosperous looking or just functional — seemed homey and peaceful.

The dairy farm — the house and outbuildings — seemed old and worn and antiquated so as to suit my own fantasy of what a farm should look like. And the cows — huge, hulking, black and white creatures, their udders swollen with milk — took me back to a childhood almost lost from memory. There were men about — big, brawny, bearded, shirtless men, who might have been authentic dairy farmers.

I read recently that there are only about 500 dairy farms surviving in Maine. There were 1,200 in 1980! So this farm, like Route 7 and the small farming villages it connects, is indeed a relic from an older, agricultural age. It was insular here; in places, the landscape took me back to George Smith's farm, or the coastal Maine landscape my widowed mother and I retreated to in 1966.

Eventually I reached I-95. Route 7 crosses that familiar landscape of fast food, motels and convenience stores before continuing north to

Newport, Corinna, Dexter and Dover-Foxcroft. It isn't as hilly or bucolic here as inland Waldo County, but now I was encountering yet another 19th century landscape of economic decline — "mill" Maine.

Beginning in Corinna and becoming more noticeable in Dexter and Dover-Foxcroft, the FOR SALE signs became ubiquitous. On some streets in Dover-Foxcroft it seemed like every other house was for sale. This is the Maine of NAFTA — of plant closings and jobs being "outsourced" to Mexico, Central America and the Pacific Rim. Here the mill towns of the 19th and early 20th centuries had collided with the global economy of the present century. It's the culmination of an old story that began in southern New England after the Civil War, when the mills closed and the plants moved to Virginia, the Carolinas and Georgia. Nevertheless, several mills had hung on in rural Maine, where labor was still relatively cheap. But how do you compete against 56 cents an hour in Honduras or El Salvador?

The drive from Belfast to Dover-Foxcroft left me plenty to think about. I still despise developers, yet I hate to see the old mill towns die. Yet they, too, were built, or "developed" by speculators. And I can scarcely imagine the feeling of hopelessness and despair after losing one's job and having to move away to find new employment. I also lament the loss of small dairy farms, yet I can appreciate the effect that the new MBNA money has had on the midcoast region.

Places change. And I, like most people in love with landscapes, simply haven't the money to buy up large tracts of Maine to preserve in a fashion that suits my particular tastes. And why should I be so arrogant as to believe my love of 19th century dairy farms and country stores and village centers should suit anybody else?

We all have different perceptions of "perfect" landscapes. To some, the ideal is pristine wilderness. To others, it's a bright, clean new subdivision, or an orderly tree farm. Still, others prefer a mix of old and new, developed and underdeveloped, which may indeed be most appropriate for a modern, free-market democracy.

As a lover of relict landscapes, I'm saddened when dairy and poultry farmers sell out. I'm saddened when textile mills, shoe and fish factories close. And all these years later, I'm still saddened that Mr. Smith sold his dairy farm and allowed the developers to destroy my childhood home. My parents and I visited Mr. Smith soon after he moved to his new farm in Freehold. But it wasn't the same. Unlike north-central New Jersey, which was heavily forested, hilly, and beautiful to me, the land around Freehold was mostly treeless and flat. As human beings shaped mostly by our pasts, some landscapes are simply more beautiful to us than others.

Flat farmland may be better suited for operating machinery. It may even seem like home to some people, but to me, those wooded, rolling hills are what stir my soul.

Freehold wasn't home to George Smith either. You could see it in his eyes. And I've often wondered if he died financially secure but spiritually impoverished.

2001

29

BEWARE OF PAPER TIGERS BUILT ON
FOOTLOOSE INDUSTRIES

I visited the Republic of Ireland in 2000, specifically Galway on the west coast and Dublin in the east.

Galway was then said to be the fastest-growing city in Europe. Dublin was in the midst of an extreme housing shortage. One could only marvel at all the construction cranes, as if some sort of economic miracle had indeed occurred. I began mentally to make comparisons between my own state of South Carolina and Ireland.

And then in January 2001, when South Carolina's economy really turned sour, I was compelled to write an opinion piece to the *State* newspaper in Columbia that began:

"In attempting to solve the state's fiscal crisis, lawmakers in South Carolina would be wise to consider the example of the Irish. Ironically, both the state of South Carolina and the Republic of Ireland have much in common. We once had slavery in South Carolina. The Irish were practically slaves of the British, before winning their independence in a civil war in 1922.

"Both South Carolina and Ireland were once primarily agrarian societies. Both places experienced decades of emigration after their agricultural economies collapsed.

"South Carolina and Ireland have small, compact shapes, served by a dense network of good roads, and populations of about 4 million. Both have mild climates with ample rainfall; subsequently, energy costs are relatively low. Finally, both are close to large, affluent markets, and have economies that rely heavily on tourism. Of course, Ireland is an island, whereas South Carolina is insular in its own ways, especially in the attitudes of some of its lawmakers.

"During the 19th and most of the 20th century, Ireland was primarily a land of emigration, which peaked during the Potato Famine of 1847-1851, when half its population either perished or left the island. Since that time, millions of Irish people have emigrated to England, Australia, East Africa, the United States and Canada. Even after independence in 1922, emigration continued as a way of life for generations of young people. Indeed, the Irish brain drain has enriched many parts of the world, including South Carolina.

"In the past decade, all that has changed. Ireland now has one of the strongest economies in Europe. The year 1999 was the first year in recent

Irish history that immigration exceeded emigration. Irish expatriates have been returning home in droves. The economy has been so strong that Ireland has taken in many refugees. Many of the low-paying service jobs — hotel clerks, maids, waiters — are now filled by immigrants from Eastern Europe.

"How did they do it? How did Ireland go from being one of the poorest countries in Western Europe to one of the most affluent? By investing in education! In a high-tech, global economy, educated workers (human capital) are the most valuable resource. Back in 1968, the Irish government began offering free university education to qualified students from low-income families. It also offered free secondary education, including state grants for private schools.

"Ireland's long-term commitment to quality education has paid off handsomely. By the 1990s a "Celtic tiger" had risen out of a landscape of chronic poverty and unemployment. Today, Ireland's economy is booming, caused in large part by increased foreign investment, attracted by government incentives, relatively few regulations, and one of the best-educated and highly motivated labor forces in Europe. Industry is expanding at an unprecedented pace. And these are high-paying jobs that have helped to create a large middle class."

Although I still believe a case can be made for turning South Carolina into a high-tech economic tiger, I have been wondering recently if a similar case can be made for Maine. In a 21st century economy, does geography even matter? But I also wonder if those economic tigers, built mostly upon footloose, high-tech industries, will endure over time. Wouldn't economies built upon a broader base of both traditional and footloose industries be better positioned to survive a downturn?

In an opinion piece published in the August 28-September 3 issue of the *Downeast Coastal Press*, Amity Shlaes, a columnist for the *Financial Times of London*, suggested that "A Tiger Slumbers in Maine's Northern Woods." Shlaes argued that by dramatically cutting taxes, Maine, too, had the potential to become an economic tiger like Ireland.

As a geographer interested in economic patterns, I was quite taken with Shlaes' essay. It forced me to ask the question, Does geography still matter in the new economy? So many of the new high-tech industries are "footloose," meaning they are able to locate practically anywhere, since they depend mostly on skilled labor (human capital) rather than raw materials.

MBNA's success in midcoast Maine is one such example. Indeed, could Maine, by "cutting state spending and taxation dramatically" as Shlaes suggests, become another Silicon Valley or a Celtic tiger?

I decided to go back to the basics. Economic geographers commonly cite 10 "golden rules" necessary to attract a critical mass of high-tech companies to a given locality: (1) proximity to a university with a graduate engineering program, (2) proximity to a cosmopolitan urban center, (3) a large pool of skilled and semiskilled labor, (4) 300 days of sunshine a year, (5) recreational water an hour away, (6) affordable nearby housing, (7) prestigious luxury housing for executives, (8) $1 billion start-up capital to lure new high-tech firms, (9) lower than normal risk for establishing profitable high-tech businesses, and (10) a cooperative spirit among landowners, lenders and government.

What is interesting is the role that amenities, both cultural and natural, play in attracting high-tech industries. And although neither Maine nor Ireland can count on 300 days of annual sunshine (even South Carolina can't count on that many!), they both possess many amenities.

Still, northern and eastern Maine have some serious geographical liabilities that Ireland, because it is on the western, or windward side of Europe, escapes. The "northern syndrome" that Shlaes writes about ("that colder weather, longer distances, poorer people — in short, the northern syndrome — excuse Maine from competition and explain all") might be better termed the "leeward syndrome," or better yet, the "Siberian effect."

Maine is a middle latitude state lying on the leeward or eastern side of a huge continent. The prevailing winds at Maine's latitude blow from the north and west, out of Canada and the continental interior, bringing severe cold in winter and high heat in summer. Ireland receives the prevailing winds coming off the ocean, which moderates its temperatures. It averages a balmy 45 degrees in January and about 65 degrees in July. Consequently, energy costs for both heating and cooling are much higher in Maine. High energy costs are not necessarily the kiss of death, however. Minnesota, with greater continentality, hence colder winters and hotter summers than Maine, has a robust economy. So does the Canadian province of Ontario.

Both Maine and Ireland lie on the edges of major economic core regions, Megalopolis and Western Europe, respectively. This is a great advantage. Indeed, Megalopolis, the eastern seaboard from Washington, D.C., to Boston, contains approximately one-fifth of the country's population and several of the states with the highest per capita incomes. Megalopolis and the European core are among the world's largest markets. Southern, and even central Maine, with their dense network of roads, are nicely positioned to feed off that huge market.

Northern and eastern Maine, however, have a serious time-distance-decay problem. Simply put, it takes time and money to overcome the "friction" of distance. It is a problem common to countries with elongated shapes such as Chile, Vietnam and Italy, and to those such as Canada and the Scandinavian countries that extend into higher latitudes. Even in prosperous Italy, the contrasts between the affluent north (close to Europe's economic core) and the impoverished south (closer to Africa) are striking.

The "Two Maine Effect" is largely about overcoming distance. How often do people in southern or eastern Maine get up to Fort Kent? Ireland, on the other hand, has a nice compact shape with a dense network of good roads connecting its towns and cities.

The answer for northern and eastern Maine, it would seem then, is to build more roads. What's become of the much touted east-west highway plan? Here again, though, Maine, because of its leeward continental position, is at a serious disadvantage. Maine's glaciated landscape freezes hard in winter. Come spring, rocks are popping up through the pavement. Pothole season has arrived! Without costly maintenance, roads in Maine quickly turn to rubble.

Unfortunately, the state hasn't the money to maintain the existing system of roads. I'm not an environmental determinist. I know that difficult environments can be overcome; the problem is, the costs sometimes outweigh the economic benefits.

So I think that the "northern syndrome," or "Siberian effect," as I prefer to call it, is real. Geography still matters. It matters more now than ever. Because...in a global economy, fortunes and circumstances change so rapidly that places like Maine that have been slow to adapt tend to fall even farther behind...to the point where most sensible folks wonder if there's even any point in trying to become the next Celtic tiger...whose own heyday may have already passed.

In recent years, the city of Bangalore in the state of Karnataka has been dubbed India's "Silicon Plateau." Several hundred software companies are based there, including IBM, Texas Instruments, and Motorola, a stern reminder that footloose industries are just that — here today, gone tomorrow!

It would not surprise me if India eventually puts Ireland out of business. India apparently has an almost limitless supply of highly skilled software engineers (remember they have a billion people) who earn about a fifth as much money as their counterparts in Europe or the United States. Ireland may once again be counting its blessings that it still has castles and coastlines and cozy pubs.

Closer to home, American Airlines moved its data entry operation to Barbados in the Caribbean back in 1984. Jamaica is said to have 25 data processing firms that employ mostly young women ("high-tech in high heels," as they're known in the academic literature) at a fraction of the wages paid at MBNA. More and more footloose industries are following the lead of the textile and apparel companies and shifting their operations to developing countries with lower operating costs.

The Caribbean may eventually challenge California's Silicon Valley, another place where labor and housing costs have become prohibitive. South Carolina is a low-tax, low-wage, low-energy-cost state, but this still hasn't kept companies from leaving us in droves. It is simply more profitable to relocate some industries to low-wage developing countries. That's the harsh reality of global capitalism. When competition is cut-throat, industries become footloose by necessity.

Meanwhile, Maine might as well follow Shlaes' advice and "cut state spending and taxation drastically." Why not try it? This might be an incentive for footloose industries such as MBNA to stick around a while longer.

2001

30

DENNY BUYS A BRAND NEW LEXUS

Denny telephoned me on New Year's Day.

"Hey, boy, when you goin' to run?"

"In about 45 minutes," I said. "I thought you ran this morning."

"No, I went to work at the mill. I need to work some overtime."

"Oh?"

"I'll tell you about it on the run."

This must be big news, I thought. Denny and I run together on weekday afternoons, but he always runs in the morning on holidays and weekends.

"I spent some money," Denny said, obviously trying to pique my curiousity.

"Oh?"

"I bought a new Lexus!"

"Yeah?"

I had to admit, I really didn't know what a Lexus was. I knew it was an expensive car, but nothing else.

"Who makes it?"

"It's made by Toyota," Denny explained. That didn't help me very much, so I logged on to the Internet and read the Lexus Web site.

August 1983

At a top-level, top-secret meeting, Toyota Chairman Eiji Toyoda determines the time is right to create a luxury vehicle to challenge the world's best.

January 1989

The LS 400 and ES 250 are unveiled to the world at Detroit and Los Angeles auto shows.

September 1989

The LS 400 and ES 250 go on sale.

February 1990

The Motoring Press Association names the LS 400 Best Imported Car of the Year.

(Between 1990 and 1999 Lexus cars won numerous awards.)

November 1999

Lexus sells its millionth vehicle in the United States.

We ran around the park, all the while Denny telling me about this amazing new automobile. All the while I'm wondering why he wanted this thing. Surely it had cost him an arm and a leg. According to the Web site, you can pay anywhere from $30,000 to well over $60,000 for a new Lexus, depending on the model and its accessories. Denny said the taxes alone were going to be more than $1,200. Car taxes are high in South Carolina. I paid $142 this year on my '94 Ford Taurus.

"So when can I see this new Lexus?"

"Wednesday."

"Oh, you and Rhonda are driving over to Columbia to get it on Wednesday? "

"No. No. When you buy a new Lexus, they deliver it to your home!"

"Oh."

"Yeah, man. And when you need to get it serviced, they leave you with another Lexus to drive until they get yours back to you!"

"Wow!" I marveled. Denny was telling me about a lifestyle I could scarcely comprehend. When I first met Denny 16 years ago, he and Rhonda had a Honda Accord. Denny also had a small Toyota pickup truck that he drove to the mill. Rhonda eventually got a company car from the bank, where she works as a loan officer. In the early '90s, they traded the Honda Accord for a Ford Explorer, and then four or five years ago, they traded up to a luxury model Explorer with an Eddie Bauer interior. Denny recently bought a new Ford Ranger pickup.

"We've got four vehicles now," Denny said. "I guess I'm gonna sell my pickup."

"So you'll drive the Explorer to work?"

"I think so, Allan. We'll probably just use the Lexus on weekends when we drive to the beach. That and for vacations."

Denny and Rhonda built a new beach house in the late '90s. That's their weekend getaway. They're "empty nesters." Their son, an only child, has been on his own for several years. He finally got married a year ago, and Denny and Rhonda paid for the wedding trip, a week at a Sandals Resort in Jamaica. Denny said that set him back more than $4,000.

Denny and Rhonda are both 52. They got married the summer they graduated from high school and have been married ever since. Neither went to college, but both have worked very hard all of their lives and now they're financially secure — I would say, quite well-off — and looking ahead to retirement.

Denny spent the entire year of 1969 fighting in Vietnam. He was in the Army, in an artillery unit. When he talks, it sometimes seems like he's hollering at you. Perhaps it's a combination of the artillery and more than 25 years of working in a noisy paper mill.

Denny is a natural athlete. He has a black belt in karate, is a certified scuba diver, and is a very good long-distance runner. He can still run a six-minute mile. He's also a deacon in the Baptist Church. He and Rhonda are pillars of the community. They seem to know everybody in town and get invited to nearly everything. They are kind and generous with their time and money. I consider them among my best friends.

But as a teacher who lived paycheck to paycheck for many years, I have to admit I'm a little uncomfortable with Denny's and Rhonda's style of conspicuous consumption. Still, Denny is always quick to remind me: "Look here, Allan, if everyone was as tight as you, this country would always be in a depression." And he's probably right.

Indeed, Thoreau has always been my mentor. I've tried to make do with less rather than more. I just don't "get" this idea of the "American dream." I'm too bleak, too grim, too fiscally conservative or something. Like a *Peanuts* character, a dark cloud is always hovering over my head. Perhaps I need to lighten up.

But I also wonder: How are we ever going to get out of this mess? If consumer spending is what drives the American economy, then where is this all going to lead? Economists warn that Americans are drowning in debt; that we may not able to spend our way out of the current recession.

Bob Sargent, a Steuben, Maine, mechanic, told me more than 20 years ago that you never get your money's worth out of a car. I believed him. I still do. New cars depreciate the moment you drive them home. They're a bad investment. But I didn't say any of this to Denny. I didn't think there was any point.

"You can't take all that money with you, Allan."

"You're right about that, Denny. That's what my father always said. He died of a heart attack at age 48."

"You see? You've got to spend it while you've got it."

In many respects, Denny represents the heart and soul of America, in that he wants all the trappings of an upper-middle-class lifestyle, and he also wants the best. Indeed, if he's going to pay top dollar for a luxury automobile, he wants the best return for that dollar.

"These cars really hold their value," Denny explained. "You can pay almost as much for a used Lexus as for a new one."

Never mind that Ford Motor Company is eliminating 35,000 jobs and discontinuing several models, including the Lincoln Continental and the once-popular Escort. The United States is the world's largest bastion of free-market capitalism. This country stands for competition. And even though Denny just put a sword through the hearts of 35,000 Ford employees, in the long run, wasn't it for the best? Either build the best automobiles, or lose the business. After all, it's just business.

Still, my heart goes out to those 35,000 Ford employees. Capitalism has always seemed excessively harsh to me. Would I be happier with socialism or communism? Not on your life. What if my commute to work were a trans-Atlantic flight? Wouldn't I rather be flying in a Lexus? Denny, the consummate consumer, is usually right about these things.

"That dash is real mahogany," Denny explained when his new Lexus finally arrived. I ran him home from the park that day, just so I could see this thing. And it was beautiful.

"Oh, I love that color, Denny!" It was "millennium" silver. "And those tires and rims...oh, man, that's a nice car!"

"It's got a separate climate control for both the driver's side and the passenger's side. Rhonda likes it a little warmer than I do. And those are special headlights so you can see much farther in the night."

"All-leather interior," I added.

"Oh, yeah, man, and you see that console there?"

"It looks like the instrument panel on a jetliner," I said.

Denny beamed. "Let me go in the house and get my computerized key. You can't get into this car without it. See, the trunk doesn't even have a lock."

Denny pressed a tiny button on his key and the door opened. Another button opened the trunk, another the gas compartment.

"Amazing," I said. "I've never seen anything like that in my life. You won't want to take it out in the rain. Really, it would be a shame to get it dirty."

"I know it," Denny said with a big smile. We both stood there in silence and just stared at his new Lexus.

2002

31

SAVORING THE SOLITUDE OF A MAINE SPRING

I have to admit I haven't actually been swimming since I arrived at camp on Jones Pond in West Gouldsboro on the 14th of May. I have, briefly, immersed myself in its icy waters after my daily run.

At first, the cold water made my head throb, as I quickly washed my hair, bracing myself against the March-like wind. Like a doomed foot soldier advancing against a hail of bullets, I'd reluctantly wade forward before suddenly lowering myself into the frigid pond. Aah! Extreme discomfort.

Call it pain — but wait. What about austerity, voluntary simplicity, purification? Such a lot of nonsense. So much for new-age, retro-hippy, Walden Pond, Mother Earth, polar-bear-club-hooey. The water is cold. And I'm an idiot for getting in it. Let's just leave it at that.

I'm all alone here, except for Bess, my obstinate, obsessive-compulsive-nuisance-of-a Border-Collie. She bit my brother-in-law during our brief stopover in New Jersey. Talk about wearing out your welcome. What can I say? I feel like a caged animal in that suburban rat race myself. Still, as Barbara Woodhouse, the celebrated British dog trainer, used to say, "There are no bad dogs, only bad owners."

Imagine if I'd had children. No, I can't even imagine it. I've always thought it ought to be against the law for college professors to have children. Lord knows, some of us are barely capable of looking after ourselves, let alone offspring.

Poor Bessie. I forgive her for all her sins.

Linda, my wife, is still teaching. She's not due here until the end of the month. I miss her for many reasons, not the least of which is I can't cook. I can burn meat on the charcoal grill, but that's rusted through and the purchase of a new one requires Linda's input. Ours is a marriage. "Big purchases" are discussed.

One day, I got so hungry for hot food that I drove Bess to Ellsworth, me drooling all the way at the thought of "rotisserie chicken" at Shaw's Supermarket.

"They'll be ready in six minutes," the pleasant woman in the deli remarked.

"Oh, good!" I was barely able to contain my excitement. "I'll swing back after I do the rest of my shopping." I love grocery stores. I go three or four times a week in South Carolina. And since we've got no refrigeration at camp other than an ice chest, I get to go every day. Is it any wonder I wrote my doctoral dissertation, and later a book, on country stores?

"Listen here, old Bess-a-fur," I said as I got back into the car. "Ro...Tiss...Erie CHICKEN! We're gonna think we've died and gone to heaven!"

For all I know, I'm already in heaven. This is my second spring. In late January, I watched the first daffodils bloom in Marion, South Carolina. The forsythia followed, then the azaleas and dogwoods peaked in March. In April, I began seeing snakes flattened on the roads. Out of those ditches alongside the highway slither cottonmouths as big around as the back tires of Harley Davidsons, 5-foot-long rattlers and exquisitely painted copperheads that strike only if you step on them. So by April, I'm confined to running in town, seeking shade, trying to avoid the debilitating effects of 90-degree temperatures.

For some reason, I had longed for the icy chill of a Maine spring more than ever this year. I got it! I had announced to my chairman back in January that I would not be teaching the three-week-intensive May course. I'd be leaving on May 10 to visit my 87-year-old mother during the Mother's Day weekend, then spending three glorious months in Maine, with no electricity, telephone, e-mail, or indoor plumbing — nothing except kerosene lamps, a woodstove and a tiny Coleman gas camping stove.

Electricity is certainly in our future, but neither of us is what you'd call "impulsive." Maybe around 2010? 2015? Linda and I were extremely poor for at least the first 10 years of our marriage. I'm not sure that's a bad thing. It's made us appreciate everything we have.

This is my other life, a season of solitude when I try to understand the world and my tiny presence in it. From now until early August, I'll spend much of the day reading all sorts of esoteric material — some of it deadly — that I've set aside during the busy academic year. I am a professor, after all. I've got to have something to "profess" and to write about the rest of the year. This camp is, foremost, a place of work.

Indeed, most of the course preparation and scholarship I've produced over the years — the vital stuff that got me tenure and promotions — was first scribbled here, in longhand, on yellow legal pads. Even now, at age 51, this still seems like an unorthodox way to earn a good living.

It is hardly the life I envisioned as a student at Sumner High School. Back then it was all sports, hunting and fishing, boats and motorcycles. A poor student and a late bloomer, I eventually stumbled into the academic life and found it suited me so much, I often have to pinch myself. And this is the best part — reading and writing in my favorite spot on earth and no classes to meet until August.

The single layer of three-quarter-inch cedar board and batten siding is aging and losing its knots. There must be a dozen or so holes that I need to patch. These are especially evident as I awaken chilled to the bone, squinting at the rays of sunlight filtering through. It's about 40 degrees in here. There's no point in building a morning fire in the stove. It's warmer eating my breakfast outside in the sun. The wood I cut and split the previous summer is saved for a nice long fire in the evening while Bess and I listen to the calling of the loons and the chorus of peepers.

A day or two after the cold Saturday rain of May 18th, I began to see the first maple and oak leaves sprout. How quickly the buds open! The morning sunlight glinting across the heath, illuminating the brilliant green young leaves of the aspens and poplars and the delicate white flowers of the sugar pears, steals my breath away.

Bess and I take long walks on the dirt road and along four-wheeler trails through the woods. All I can do is marvel. I haven't been here this early in the spring since 1988. This is, for me, the rarest of treats. But like all of life's wonders, such extraordinary beauty is fleeting.

Soon, the apple trees along the dirt road will blossom; next to bloom are the lilacs. It won't be long now until Linda arrives. I have a wife of 27 years whom I miss terribly, and I mark the days on the calendar like a high school senior anticipating graduation. I can hardly wait to drive to Bangor and greet her at the airport. What will I say?

"Hi you, Bud."

"Hi, yourself."

"Uh. Somebody's waiting for you in the car."

"Oooh!"

There'll be a furry body wiggling, a tail wagging and lots of ear licking.

In a few weeks, the daisies and the Indian paintbrush will light up the fields, and the mosquitoes will replace the blackflies. The bullfrogs will dominate the vanishing peepers, and cars and trucks and motorcycles with out-of-state licenses will clog Route 1. In the meantime, I'm savoring the solitude of a Maine spring.

2002

32

IMAGINING MAINE

The philosopher, Edward S. Casey, suggests that: "Places come into us lastingly; once having been in a particular place for any considerable time — or even briefly, if our experience there has been intense — we are forever marked by that place, which lingers in us indefinitely and in a thousand ways, many too subtle for us to name. The inscription is not of edges or outlines, as if the place were some kind of object; it is the whole brute presence of the place. What lingers most powerfully is this presence and, more particularly, how it felt to be in this presence: how it felt to be in the Crazy Mountains that summer, how I sensed the lower east side during January.

"Proust points out that the essence of a place can be compressed into a single sensation, which, being reawakened, can bring the place back to us in its full vivacity. There is an impressionism of place by which the presence of a place remains lodged in our body long after we have left it; this presence is held within the body in a virtual state, ready to be revived when the appropriate impression or sensation arises."

How do Mainers imagine Maine? How does the rest of America perceive this state? And why, in a country with more than 285 million people, do only a million or so live in Maine? These are pertinent questions, ones our planners, political aspirants, and lawmakers should be asking. Most Mainers, obviously, love their state or they wouldn't live here. And millions of other Americans would probably reside here if they could find gainful employment.

Indeed, politicians and others have argued recently that if Maine had a better-educated (i.e., college-educated) labor force it would attract new industry. Others have argued that by cutting taxes, Maine could be more competitive. Still, others have suggested that a better system of roads — especially the construction of a new, high-speed, east-west highway — would make Maine more competitive and more attractive to new industries. All of these are valid arguments. I do not want to take issue with any of these.

What I intend to argue is that Maine's faltering economy has as much to do with the way Mainers and other Americans imagine the state as it does with economics or geography. Simply put, I believe there are many Americans — including those with the capital to start companies and small businesses — who prefer to imagine Maine as something other than a good place to make money. Perhaps they'd rather see it as a good place for artists, musicians, poets, writers and dreamers. Maybe they'd prefer to see it as the home of rugged individualists — hunters, fishermen, boat builders, loggers, organic farmers, worm diggers, stock car racers. Perhaps they have a more romantic than utilitarian image of Maine. Perhaps many Mainers have a similar image of their state.

All of us have our own ideas of what places really are, and what their futures should be. We don't all see the same geography. And I rather doubt that the Maine the state's politicians perceive is the one imagined by many of its residents, or by many other Americans. Images of places are not only powerful, they're enduring; it takes decades, sometimes generations, to change people's perceptions of places, especially those that are dear to them. For many Americans, Maine has a special mystique, gotten as much from literature, movies and art, as from reality.

Certainly it can be argued that mid-coast Maine has The Jackson Laboratory and MBNA, and there are several cutting-edge and high-tech industries in southern Maine; still, much of the north and east is imagined as a resource-based region where rugged individualists scratch a living as best they can. Perhaps this is the way it should be. Maybe "two Maines" are better than one. Perhaps the mettle to survive in the "County" or in "the other state of Maine" is a point of pride. Do Mainers really want to transform Aroostook, Penobscot, Piscataquis or Washington counties into Cumberland or York? Maybe a million Mainers, or even 800,000 is quite enough. After all, midcoast and southern Maine are already plagued by sprawl and traffic congestion.

I'm guessing that most of those folks who have found ways to earn a living in northern or eastern Maine would say they like most things about it (Oh, they'd like to make more money and pay less taxes), and if it got like Portland, Camden, Belfast or Bar Harbor, it just wouldn't be the same. Its unique character would be lost. They might not be able to live there anymore, especially if it became a Camden or Bar Harbor.

By its very nature, capitalism creates changing geographies of uneven development. There isn't a region or country on earth without backwaters. But quite often it is those very places — think of Scotland or Wales, or even Ireland before the already fading "Celtic Tiger" boom — that leave lasting impressions on visitors, and inspire local artists and writers. Think of Frank McCourt's magnificant memoir *Angela's Ashes* or Carolyn Chute's gritty novel *The Beans of Egypt, Maine*. Those backwaters, because of timelessness of their landscapes, because of the uniqueness of their cultures, continue to draw people back, leaving an indelible image on their souls. Who would want to visit Nova Scotia, Prince Edward Island, New Brunswick or Newfoundland if their landscapes and cultures resembled the Ontario peninsula, with its automobile plants and industrial suburbs? The lure of northern and eastern Maine is that it is not a southern California, a New Jersey or a southern Ontario.

Instead of bemoaning the economic stagnation of northern and eastern Maine, we should be celebrating its uniqueness. Despite those thousands of Mainers — like me — who have left home to pursue opportunities elsewhere, there are still thousands of others who lead quiet, productive, satisfying lives in places like Steuben, Whiting, Winn and Wytopitlock. We can't always have our cake and eat it too. I have former high school classmates who now live in Florida, the Bahamas and other states and countries. Are they pining for home? Not hardly. Many of them pity the classmates they left behind, while those remaining pity them for having to leave.

All states, regardless of the size of their economies, experience brain drains. California's outmigration is huge. College graduates are often bright, ambitious and curious about other cultures and places. Why hold them back? Ours is a big, fascinating country. Some of them will return home anyway, once they've had their fill of those places, once they've matured and acquired skills and experiences they can use in Maine. And when they do return, what is it that pleases them so much? That breathtaking landscape still looks pretty much the same. It hasn't yet been transformed into Orlando, or Anaheim or Silicon Valley. And that unique culture, that indefatigable character and spirit, that is rooted in the rock and soil of Maine, is still very much intact.

2002

33

BURNIN' RUBBER

I was filling my gas tank at Mathews Country Store in Steuben when two young men in a Camaro or Firebird or similar muscle car pulled out onto Route 1. They stopped suddenly, looked to see there were no approaching cars, then stomped on 'er. There was a loud roar, a cloud of black smoke, the smell of burning rubber, then the high-pitched whine of squealing tires as they fishtailed into the oncoming lane before barreling down Route 1. My wife, Linda, just laughed. She said, "All these years I've seen the tire marks on the road around here, but that's the first time I've ever seen anyone do it."

Indeed, just a half mile or so east of Mathews, near where the old Ponderosa Take-Out used to be (the empty building still stands), the highway is a sinuous web of "signatures." Some things never change. More than 30 years ago when I was in high school that stretch of pavement looked exactly the same. "That's some of Bub's work," a friend might say. Or, "Scotty left that patch of rubber last night. Geez, didn't he come on to 'er!" These are highly personal signatures in a subculture that has always reveled in speed, power and noise.

But some things have changed. Thirty years ago, when local boys burned rubber, they might have had their sights on winning a trophy at the Winterport Dragway. These days a young guy with a hot rod likely has bigger dreams — maybe even racing in the Winston Cup.

Stockcar racing has become mainstream, perhaps even eclipsing baseball or basketball as rural America's "field of dreams." Thirty years ago we idolized Carl Yastremski; now we idolize Ricky Craven. Indeed, Ricky has shown us that a guy from rural Maine can run with the best that NASCAR has to offer. And that goal may seem more obtainable and desirable nowadays than a career in professional baseball or basketball.

Sports has changed, the ethnic and racial composition of the country has changed, traditional gender roles have changed. As well they should — those barriers had to come down, sports had to be integrated, women athletes deserved equal status with men. The barriers that women and minorities faced were enormous. Jackie Robinson, Joan Benoit, Cindy Blodgett, Mia Hamm, Tiger Woods, the Williams sisters — they all shattered barriers; they all deserve our praise and recognition.

But even though Title IX raised the status of women athletes, we still don't know its long-term effect on traditional gender roles. Gone are the days when schoolboy baseball and basketball stars got all the glory. Now they compete for space in the sports pages with the girls. There's still that age-old biological problem—male testosterone—not to mention ego. And what about the boys who are only marginal athletes, who are not part of the jock and cheerleader culture? Has Title IX diminished them even more? Has this group become even more alienated from the sports culture of the typical American high school? For many rural boys, identifying themselves through the horsepower of their machines has been their only salvation, their only taste of glory.

Gone, too, are the days when a white man from Southern California could bat 406 against all white pitchers and be called "the greatest hitter of all time." Today he's got to bat against African-American, Hispanic and Asian pitchers as well. The chances of a medium-sized kid from Cherryfield, Caribou, Bangor or Bar Harbor making it to the NBA or the Major Leagues seem slimmer than ever. Today it seems like runners and jumpers and hitters and hurlers are competing against athletes from the entire world. Dreams can be dashed in the blink of an eye.

Not so with stockcar racing. I believe that stockcar racing has become America's fastest-growing sport for two main reasons: it is still local and it is wholly American. It began with Depression-era moonshine runners in the coves and hollows of southern Appalachia and has since captured the imaginations of independent-minded men and women in every nook and cranny of the nation.

Consider Ricky Craven, or Cherryfield's rising sensation, Andy Santerre. These days many of us find ourselves paying more attention to their pole positions than to Pedro Martinez's earned run average. Could this be because Ricky or Andy seems more like us? Here is an average guy from a small Maine town pitting his nerves, reflexes and driving skills against similar American men from similar towns. All this is in stark contrast to the increasingly dull, programmed, post-industrial world we inhabit. Who among us doesn't crave some excitement?

The racecar driver has courage. He's a risk-taker. Still, he's not some superman with a perfect body. Nor is he some sinewy young soccer player ripping off her jersey and prancing around in her sports bra. How many of us can even remember her name? I can't. All I remember is the photograph in the sports pages — the nubile young woman in the sports bra. For me, a middle-aged white male, the image was purely sexual. Nothing more. Soccer, the world's most popular sport, was not part of my childhood. I have a hard time relating to it.

But local boys, whose names and families we know, who begin racing locally with sponsors like Young's Market or Parritt's Auto Body, and who eventually win it all at Speedway 95 or Oxford or Unity and earn a "ride" in the Busch North — we can identify with them. They were the teen-agers who once left their signatures on Route 1. Now we look for their names in the weekly points totals. Maybe some day their picture will adorn the Pepsi machine outside Mathews Country Store. After all, dreams are what make life bearable.

And for the most part, these good ol' boys are just that — decent, hardworking, ordinary American men. They tend to be good role models for their fans, who are among the most fiercely local of any sport.

When Dale Earnhardt died at Daytona Speedway in February 2001, condolence registers appeared in scores of funeral homes across the Carolinas. Race fans by the tens of thousands came to pay their respects. Thousands more brought flowers to the region's NASCAR Cafes and racetracks. Earnhardt's passing was the leading news story for more than a week. I've never seen so many grown men and women cry. The South had not witnessed such an outpouring of grief and sympathy since the passing of Elvis in August of 1977.

But in many ways, Earnhardt's stature is eclipsing that of Elvis, who died prematurely of drugs and a life of excess. Earnhardt died on the job. We saw him as an ordinary working man, performing better at his job than most of us do at our own. Dale Earnhardt never even went to high school. He simply went to work. No wonder millions of Americans identified with him.

Hemingway once wrote that there are only three sports that matter — boxing, bullfighting and automobile racing. Indeed, confronting danger and possibly even death, is daunting. Maybe, then, a patch of rubber left on Route 1 in Steuben, Maine, is — in a small, symbolic way — a brush with one's own mortality.

2002

RUNNING THE PERRY TO EASTPORT
— 7-MILE RACE — 33 YEARS LATER

"You could take up swimming," an orthopedic surgeon said to me last winter. "But I know runners. We could go in there arthroscopically, but you might not notice any improvement. You've hardly got any cartilage in that knee." He pointed to the X-rays.

"You see what I mean?" It made me think of brake pads — one good, the other worn down to nothing. "And those are arthritis spurs," the doctor continued, pointing to four places on the X-ray.

Then he examined the bad knee manually.

"Does this hurt?"

"No."

"How about this?"

"No."

"Well, you don't have any torn ligaments. I'd continue with the glucosamine-chondroitin supplements and try taking some Aleve. If you get so you can't run at all, then come back and we'll try to do something."

"I'm still running about 50 miles a week," I said. The orthopedic surgeon smiled sympathetically.

Long distance running is an addiction as severe as alcohol or drugs. I like to think of it as a positive addiction — like stockcar racing — in that it might keep you from harming yourself in some other crazy way. Indeed, without a sympathetic and supportive spouse, running would destroy even the most promising relationship.

Since first running the Boston Marathon as a high school senior in 1969, I've run 53 marathons and averaged more than 3,000 miles a year. I can't quite straighten out my right leg. I can feel the bones in my bad knee rubbing together. And when I run along Route 1 in Gouldsboro in the summer, people in passing cars sometimes point at me. I imagine them saying something like, "Oh, look at that poor man. He looks like he's in pain."

He is. They should see me try to get out of a car after a long ride.

I've run more than 100,000 miles since 1969. Seven of those miles were run from Perry to Eastport in 1970; seven more were run on July 5, 2003.

The Charles E. Davis 7-Mile Memorial Road Race is one of the oldest races in Maine. When I told John Marshall, the race director, that I'd run the original 1970 race, he looked at me as though I were an apparition.

"Dale Lincoln was the race director back then," I said.

I chatted a while with Bruce Bridgham, a veteran runner from Jonesboro, when suddenly I spotted a vaguely familiar figure. "Bruce, that white-haired fellow...is that... is that Dale Lincoln?"

"That's him," Bruce said.

When I introduced myself, Dale said, "I've been looking for you! I've got something for ya. Wait here a minute."

Dale returned in a few minutes with a book. "Can you find yourself in that picture?" he asked. On page 313 of Dale's wonderful book, *Clyde Found Fruitflies in the Berries*, there's a photograph of the starting line of the 1970 race.

"That's me in the second row," I said. All you could see was a mop of blond, strawlike hair. On the next page there's a listing of the 16 finishers with their names, hometowns and finishing times. Eleventh place: Clifford Lockyer, Steuben, 53:07.

I've always used my middle name, Allan, but I wrote my first name on the entry blank because I wanted it to be official. Clifford was the name on my driver's license.

Thirty-three years ago! I was 19. But I remember that race as though it were yesterday. I had ridden down to Eastport on my Yamaha motorcycle. I wore a white tee-shirt, a sweatband, shorts and a pair of running shoes that were a size too large.

I had just completed my freshman year of college in Arkansas. I ran cross country and the two-mile in track. I was a walk-on, not a scholarship runner. My best two-mile was 11:19. I routinely got lapped.

Occasionally, if we ran against a college that didn't have many distance runners, I could score a point just for finishing. And once, when my college was tied with another school, the outcome of the meet came down to the two-mile. I remember my teammates on the sidelines yelling at me, "Allan! Don't quit! We need your point to win the meet." I had no business trying to run college track; no talent, only determination.

I had also met a girl that freshman year. And that summer, I waited anxiously for her letters, wondering if I was in deeper than she. She was from Arkansas and a sophomore. I was a marginal student, to boot. A "C" was a good grade for me. I wondered if she'd come to her senses and had dumped me for someone with better prospects. Such insecurities! I wouldn't want to be 19 again.

The 1970 Perry to Eastport race did not go well. I went out too fast. And about midway, after the sun had burned through the fog, I began to "hit the wall." The last few miles were torture. I went all wobbly and came staggering across the finish line in 53 minutes.

And there was my mother! She'd surprised me. She'd driven down from Steuben with one of her friends. It seems incredible to me now, but my mother was 55 then, just three years older than I am now.

"Allan!" A girl I'd known at Sumner High School suddenly approached me. I was all doubled over, exhausted, panting and embarrassed, not knowing what to say to this girl, my mother or my mother's friend. All I could think about was how badly I'd run and how much I missed the girl back in Arkansas.

In 1992, the year I turned 41, I ran 103 miles one week. Between 1975 and 1999, I averaged nearly 3,500 miles a year. I ran a 2:44 personal best in the 1975 Boston Marathon and was still running three-hour marathons in my early 40s.

But in the summer of 1999 I tripped while running on Route 1 in Gouldsboro and my kneecap hit the pavement. I haven't been able to run a marathon since.

I'm not sure why it took me so long to get back to Eastport. It's 85 miles from Gouldsboro, and by the late 1970s there were plenty of road races here in Hancock County. I've been haunted this summer, though, by something my mother said this past winter. "You won't be able to do that much longer," she'd said in late January, when I told her I had just run the North Myrtle Beach 15K race. I hadn't told her about my visit to the orthopedic surgeon, either.

The 2003 Perry to Eastport run was like deja vu. Once again, we rode a school bus out to the start. I sat next to Bruce Bridgham, who at age 43 would win the race in 40 minutes. Dale Lincoln, who completed the four-mile walk, sat behind us.

It was warm and foggy. I carried a 20-ounce bottle of water that I sipped on the way to Perry. We stopped four miles from Eastport to let off the walkers. That left about 40 of us, all ages, mostly men, and about a half-dozen women, some of them crewmembers from the USS Ticonderoga.

I stretched and drank some more water in Perry, and soon we were off. The state trooper who escorted us asked that we run the first few miles on the right side of the road, which really aggravated my bad knee.

I started out at a conservative 7:30 per mile pace, somewhere in the middle of the pack. The fog lingered; the sun held off. It was cooler than 1970. We began the long series of climbs past Pleasant Point Indian reservation. I was less anxious than in 1970. I paced myself. I even managed to pass a few runners; they just sort of came back to me.

As we got into Eastport, I caught up to Dale, who was nearing the end of the four-mile walk, and said, "I'm at 53 minutes right now, Dale. I'm not gonna make it." My goal had been to break my 1970 time.

"Keep it up!" Dale said. "You've only got about a quarter of a mile to go."

My mother died on May 4 at the age of 88. But this time, the girl from Arkansas, whom I married in 1975, greeted me with a big smile as I crossed the finish line in 23rd place in 55 minutes and 18 seconds.

2003

35

SMALL WILDERNESSES ARE STILL THERE
FOR THOSE WHO SEEK THEM

Because we humans prefer our creature comforts, we are drawn to scenic places that are easily accessible. We gravitate toward those areas designated as "national" or "state" or "scenic" wildernesses or parks.

It's as if we've lost the ability to recognize natural beauty on our own. We need an "authority" of sorts (a Hollywood film star, perhaps) to inform us about those destinations worth visiting. We also need decent accommodations nearby.

Indeed, there is always some truly majestic place farther east, farther west, farther north, farther inland, farther away from it all that we simply must experience. But is the long journey always worth it? Add to that the cost of food and lodging, not to mention the traffic jams caused by thousands of tourists.

Anyone who loves the outdoors has enough sense to stay away from popular state and national parks. If only we could appreciate what we have around us — the tiny wilderness that's our road, our cove, our meadow, our gravel pit, even our own backyard. All of these are more precious than some distant wilderness in Alaska, Wyoming or northern Maine.

Like many rural Americans, I need personal space. I wouldn't want to live in a city or densely populated area. But as a child growing up in north-central New Jersey in the 1950s, I always seemed to be able to find that tiny brook or that swatch of woods and fields the developers had not yet paved over.

After moving to Steuben in the 1960s, I never had to leave town to find all the wilderness I needed. Less than a mile of thick woods separating old and new Route 1 and the meadows around the bay sustained my wilderness cravings throughout my high school years. Indeed, it is really amazing how little wilderness we humans actually need. There's always so much to see. In his essay "Walking," Thoreau explained it this way:

My vicinity affords many good walks; and though for so many years I have walked almost every day, and sometimes for several days together, I have not yet exhausted them. An absolutely new prospect is a great happiness, and I can still get this any afternoon. Two or three hours' walking will carry me to as strange a country as I expect ever to see. A single farmhouse which I had not seen before is sometimes as good as the dominions of the king of Dahomey. There is in fact a sort of harmony

discoverable between the capabilities of the landscape within a
circle of 10 miles' radius, or the limits of an afternoon walk, and
the threescore years and 10 of human life. It will never become
quite familiar to you.

Especially now, as my beloved town of Gouldsboro, where I've summered since 1973, is being subdivided again and again and carved up into
pricey, exclusive waterfront lots, I can take much comfort in this small
wilderness idea.

Why is it that developers these days seem to favor gaping-wide gravel or even paved superhighways? It's as if they want to lure you down
them so you can see for yourself what a horrible mess they've made of the
once pristine landscape. Wouldn't a simple, narrow, winding, wooded
lane that followed the contours of the landscape be more inviting? Beauty
is not only a matter of aesthetics, but a matter of scale: Small is quaint;
large is crass.

Fortunately, I'm able to re-examine all this landscape devastation
each May — after another year of teaching out-of-state — while it's still
cold and raw, before the trees leaf out. I can settle into my small wilderness before the water in Jones Pond is warm enough to attract boaters or
swimmers. One can still find wilderness out of season, even in a tourist
area.

I can also take comfort in my age — 52 — knowing that I've had several years to enjoy this place before the developers had their way with it;
before the trashing of the entrance to my favorite trout stream in nearby
Steuben; before the dump truck men chained and padlocked the gravel
road leading into my second-favorite brook here in Gouldsboro.

This is what Downeast Maine has come to — a tangle of private,
sometimes padlocked, dirt roads that deny you access to a stretch of coastline (I understand it is still legal to tramp along the Maine coast...that is if
you can get to it) or to your favorite fishing holes, as if they still have any
fish. When I told the friendly game warden who checked my fishing
license recently that I hadn't caught any trout, but had seen a moose, he
said, "Well, that's worth the price of admission."

In "The American Geographies," Barry Lopez suggests that:

> If a society forgets or no longer cares where it lives, then anyone
> with the political power and the will to do so can manipulate the
> landscape to conform to social ideals or nostalgic visions. People
> may hardly notice that anything has happened, or assume that
> whatever happens — a mountain stripped of timber and eroding

into its creeks — is for the common good. The more superficial
a society's knowledge of the real dimensions of the land it occupies
becomes, the more vulnerable the land is to exploitation, to manipulation
for short-term gain. The land, virtually powerless before political and commercial entities, finds itself finally with no defenders. It finds
itself bereft of intimates with indispensable, concrete knowledge.
(Oddly, or perhaps not oddly, while American society continues to
value local knowledge as a quaint part of its heritage, it continues to
cut such people off from any real political power. This is as true for
small farmers and illiterate cowboys as it is for American Indians,
native Hawaiians and Eskimos.)

All I need is this shaded dirt road where I can walk my dog. I need
the dense brush and trees and the blackflies, deerflies and mosquitoes that
inhabit it to drive away all but the hardiest outdoorsmen and give me the
solitude I cherish. There are no "Private, Keep Out" signs here. My
neighbors and I don't want them.

A mat of green moss on a large granite rock, the riot of colors in a
meadow of June wildflowers, a small gravel pit with a tiny frog pond in
the middle where my dog can swim and cool off, mean more to me than
Acadia, Grand Canyon, Yosemite or any of our national parks.

The tiny pond in the gravel pit has minnows, but no picnickers,
swimmers or tourists. Once in a while, a local person comes down to
mine the gravel or to sight-in a hunting rifle, but most of the year this
cherished place waits patiently for my dog and me. It's nothing special,
but that's my point: We all have these quite ordinary landscapes that offer
us more pleasure on an everyday basis than those national parks and scenic vistas we're told we need to visit.

Indeed, this nondescript swatch of Gouldsboro has given me back a
thousand times more than I've ever invested in it. Why does it take us so
long to see and appreciate the smallest things in life? I guess we just have
a tendency to take what's ordinary and comforting for granted.

Meanwhile, the Gouldsboro peninsula continues to be invaded by elit-
ists who will deny locals access to beaches, but who also want to educate
us on everything from environmentalism to the merits of fine dining. I
cling to the same local restaurants, where the fish-and-chips is still the
best haddock around, and the portions are large enough to force me to
leave some on my plate. I want the most nutritious food I can find for the
lowest price. Really, that's all I can afford.

I don't want atmosphere, style or theater. I just want what's always
been here — the land and the sea, and the people who make their living
from it. That was enough for writers like Mary Ellen Chase, Ruth Moore

and Louis Dickenson Rich, a half century ago. It's more than enough for me.

2003

36

THE MANY LIVES OF GLADYS LOCKYER
February 2, 1915 - May 4, 2003

Gladys Lockyer, my mother, was born in Irvington, New Jersey on Ground Hogs Day 1915, during the Great War. She lived through the Roaring Twenties, The Great Depression, World War II, the Korean Conflict, The Cold War, Vietnam, Desert Storm, and the April 2003 Liberation of Iraq. Ironically, the number of horses and mules in the United States peaked in 1915, the very year Gladys was born. Automobiles were still a luxury that only the wealthy could afford. By 2003 there were more than 200 million motor vehicles and 287 million people in the United States. In 1900, life expectancy at birth was only 47; it was 79 for women by 2003. My mother, who died at age 88, exceeded the 2003 average by nine years.

Indeed, my mother, it always seemed to me, lived several lives. Since I didn't come along until 1951, eleven and thirteen years respectively, after my sisters, Linda and Janet, were born, my memories as Gladys' son only date back to the 1950s. There was no such thing as a child's car seat back then, so my mother always placed me in the back seat of the 1939 Ford that my parents had bought for 50 dollars from a man named Ridinsky. Ridinsky's old Ford wasn't the most reliable car, and I next remember my mother running her errands around Short Hills and Millburn, New Jersey in a 1946 Plymouth coupe that I called "Mom's Plimmer."

Gladys was an extremely active mother of two teenaged girls and the shy little boy who always stood upright in the back of the Plimmer. Early on, I realized that my mother was unusual. She just seemed to have more "get up and go" (one of her expressions) than other mothers. Mom ran her own engraving business; she tended a huge vegetable garden; she lovingly cared for dozens of varieties of flowers, shrubs, and trees, on our acre of paradise. She cooked and cleaned, and cared for my grandmother (who lived with us until her death at 91), my father, two sisters, three dogs, a cat, and me. My mother always said, "Your father loved anything on four legs." One of my father's dogs was a Great Dane named Ace. My mother always smiled and said, "I brought food out to that dog every afternoon for nine years and he never once came out of his house to acknowledge me. Ace was a one-man dog. He wouldn't let anybody near him except your father or you."

Yes, me the baby she had at age 36. I still remember my parents placing me on Ace's back and riding him as though he were a pony.

Mom was a den mother for my Cub Scout pack. She attended my school plays and Little League games. She made all of my Halloween costumes. And in the evening, for a half hour before I went to bed, she quizzed me on the Baltimore Catechism, listened while I said my prayers, then tucked me in. I can still feel the Baltimore Catechism in my hands. It had a sturdy green cover, and I'm certain that all of my Catholic guilt comes from that wonderful book. My mother made certain I never missed Mass, even while on vacation, and the "Lockyer conscience" all of us seem to have, comes, I'm sure, from that good Catholic upbringing.

As a child, and later as an adult, I never heard anybody say an unkind word about my mother. She was never one to criticize or judge others. She was always willing to forgive one's shortcomings, and most importantly, she always found something good in everybody. She even managed to find a few good things to say about Richard Nixon during the Watergate Scandal.

My mother, who painted in oils and worked with pastels, had an extraordinary eye for natural beauty. She never failed to comment on the radiance of the sunrise or sunset. She delighted in the changing landscape of all four seasons, and loved a good snowstorm, hurricane, or any unusual weather. Every day was a good day to Mom.

I have such vivid memories of walking out the front door of our house in Short Hills, New Jersey, as she saw me off to the school bus, on crisp, spring mornings. I can still smell the wisteria, which climbed to the top of a red cedar tree. I can still see the first spring crocuses and hyacinths popping out of the ground. I can see the milk box in the porch corner. I can see all this so vividly, as if it were still 1957 or 58...and then there's my mother's youthful, smiling face, her clear, warm, reassuring voice — a rich, soothing voice, that anyone who ever met her, would never forget. Why are those memories so vivid now? Already, my memories of an ailing octogenarian are fading away, already replaced by memories of that young, vibrant woman, whose sight, sensibilities, and love of life were at their peak. Such a gift we humans have — the selective memory to preserve forever all that we cherish, to quickly vanquish what we'd just as soon let go of. Like my mother's own selective memory near the end, I've pretty much forgotten the indignities of the nursing home, to once again revel in the wisteria, the crocuses, the hyacinths, the brilliant yellow of the forsythia, and the soft warmth of the rhododendron.

I think my mother must have planted every sort of flower, bush, or tree that was then available at Stump and Walter's, the garden center on Morris Turnpike. We had apples and azaleas, blackberries, black raspber-

ries, and black-eyed Susans, Bartlett pears, clematis, crocuses, chrysan-
themums, Queen Anne's Lace, Concord grapes, gladiolas, daffodils,
daisies, delphinium, dogwoods, elderberries, geraniums, Johnny-jump-
ups, goldenrod, gooseberries, hyacinths, hollyhocks, honeysuckle, horse
chestnuts, irises, lilacs, lilies, marigolds, peonies, petunias, phlox, prim-
rose, privet hedge, quince, raspberries, rhododendron, roses, rose of
Sharon, strawberries, violets, zinnias, and countless other varieties I can't
even recall. (My mother would have laughed at me now, paging through
the dictionary, trying to spell all those plants. No doubt she could have
spelled them all.) And then she'd go, "Oh, dear!" as my father, my sisters, and I sneezed our heads off...but we loved her just the same.

My mother transformed our acre at 423 White Oak Ridge Road into a
botanical garden fit for an English earl. I know my father loved it. I'm
sure it helped to lower his blood pressure. "Look at your mother," he'd
say, as he marveled at her energy. He liked to call her "Dearie." I know
he appreciated all that she did, because I never heard him criticize her or
say anything unkind about her. My parents were devoted to each other,
and it never surprised me whenever my mother said, "I knew I'd never
find another man like your father. He was so easy to live with." She was
perfectly content to live with his memory after he died.

After my father died of a massive heart attack while on vacation in
Maine in 1966, my mother began another life. I think it was only after I
had been married to my wife, Linda, for many years that I fully appreciated all that my mother must have endured those first days, weeks, and
then years after my father's death. He was 48; she was 51 — both in the
prime of their lives. I'm certain they had a wonderful marriage. I have
no recollection of arguments or fights. Oh, they could disagree — she
voted for Nixon, while Dad voted for JFK in 1960. And when I was 12,
I remember that when I stubbornly resisted going to my friend, Glenn's,
Bar Mitzvah, Mom said, "Al, you really ought to go. You're going to hurt
Glenn's feelings." "Do I have to?" I whined. "I don't want to go to some
Bar Mitzvah." My father got me off the hook. "If he doesn't want to go,
then don't make him," he said. Perhaps because my father preferred his
books, his dogs, and his yard work to social occasions, he could
empathize with me. But my mother looked me sternly in the eyes and
said, "I still think you should go, Al. You're gonna be sorry if you hurt
Glenn's feelings." I didn't go. And 40 years later I still feel guilty. You
can't outlive the Lockyer conscience.

I went to Sumner High School in East Sullivan, Maine. My mother
was a freshman at the University of Maine at Machias. I'm really not sure
why my mother decided to sell our home in Short Hills and move to

Maine. She told me recently that I was the one who convinced her to do it. "Oh, let's go to Maine," was apparently what I'd said. But I don't remember it. I think my mother was just ready to put the past behind her and start on a new life. After all, it was Mom who had traveled 12 hours by herself on a Greyhound Bus to Steuben, Maine in 1959. She had seen an advertisement in the Newark Evening News for an old farmhouse by the bay for sale at 2,800 dollars. It seemed too good to be true, but my mother never could resist a bargain, so off she went with my father's blessing to a little coastal town with 700 people, some 150 miles northeast of Portland. It was too good to be true. The house was in ruins, but just down the road was an 1830s Cape Cod house with a view of the bay that my mother bought in a split-second decision. "I only saw the kitchen," she said. "Just then the south-bound Greyhound bus went by, and I said, "Oh, there goes my bus!" My mother and the realtor jumped into his car and chased the bus down Route 1 until it finally stopped at Tuttles Store in Gouldsboro.

My parents loved the old Cape Cod house in Steuben, Maine and that became our vacation destination until my father died in 1966. I'll never know my mother's inner thoughts that first year without my father, but it was surely the worst year of my life. I especially remember a solitary walk on the mudflats at low tide one afternoon in early November. I was wearing rubber boots and it was snowing, when suddenly, I just went down. I'd fallen into a honey-pot, a quicksand-like cavity in the mudflats. I was up to my neck in ooze and the only way out was to swim. Thirty minutes later when I arrived home all caked in mud, I yelled, "Mom! Mom! Come out here!" My mother took one look at me and said, "Don't move! Let me get the camera!" It was the hardest either of us had laughed in a long time and I knew then we'd be okay in Maine.

My mother excelled in college. I remember her typing out term papers on a portable Smith-Corona. I still have that typewriter. I use it every summer at our camp in West Gouldsboro.

I remember visiting the campus in Machias one day with Mom the summer after my freshman year of college in Arkansas. It sounded so strange when college students my own age called out, "Hi, Gladys! How are your classes going?" She was in her mid-fifties...yet there was my mother, just another coed. I remember sitting in the bleachers when Mom graduated in 1972. She was 57 then, an age when most folks start thinking ahead to retirement. Not my mother! She was thinking ahead to nearly 30 more years of employment.

My mother parented by example. She wasn't afraid to fail. She wasn't afraid to take risks either. But I think one of the things I loved most about my mother was that she also had the courage to allow her children to take risks. When I announced during my junior year of high school that I was going to be a golden gloves boxer, my mother said, "Boxing? Oh, I don't know, Al. I don't think that's such a good idea." A few weeks later, on the way to the doctor's office with my shoulder dislocated, my mother simply said, "Maybe you should just rest on your laurels for a while."

In the spring of my senior year, when I announced that I was planning to run the Boston Marathon, my mother said, "Twenty-six miles? Oh, I don't know, Al. I'm not sure that's such a good idea." I remember when she picked me up at the Greyhound Bus stop. "Well! So you made it!" she beamed. My mother always insisted her children were never any trouble, but oh, what we must have put her through.

And then the summer I graduated from high school, I announced that I was riding my 350cc Yamaha motorcycle 1,800 miles from Maine to college in Arkansas. This time my mother really put her foot down (another one of her expressions). "Oh, Al. No, I don't think that's a good idea at all. Why don't you just fly down there? Maybe we can ship the motorbike." My argument was...that since I'd never been away from home before...that if I rode the bike down there on my own, I'd arrive on campus with more self-confidence. I doubt my mother ever bought that argument, but finally one day she said, "Well, why don't you write the Exxon Company, Al? Maybe they can send you some maps with the best routes for motorcycles." I still remember Mom and me at the kitchen table, pouring over those maps. No doubt some of my classmates' parents thought my mother was nuts for letting me go off on that motorcycle. But my mother always insisted that she never cared what other people thought. And once she made a decision, she stuck with it. She never second-guessed herself. "Just be sure and call me every night," she insisted. "And be very careful."

My mother lived in Maine for six years. After her college graduation, she moved to Landing, New Jersey, where she taught school for a while, before settling into a job as a tour guide and curator of the apothecary shop at Waterloo Village Restoration. My mother made several trips to Europe during her Waterloo years. She even saw the house in Hartlepool, England where my grandmother lived before coming to America in 1912. Mom worked at Waterloo Village for more than 25 years, before retiring at age 84.

This past summer, 30 years after my mother had left Maine, people there were still asking about her. Indeed, upstairs in a wood-paneled room of the Steuben, Maine Parish House, there's an oil painting of a young boy fishing in a stream. The controlled, understated style of the painting seems to fit perfectly with the elegant Victorian building...with one exception — the young boy is wearing an outlandish, wide-brimmed hat. The boy is me. When I first saw the painting, I asked my mother why I was wearing that silly hat. From my earliest recollections, my mother was always putting hats on my head. She always insisted I wear a white tee shirt while swimming at the Jersey Shore. On my forehead today there is a scar the size of a quarter, where a few years ago, a skin cancer had to be surgically removed. I guess from the very beginning, my mother had tried to preserve me, the way she had always preserved herself.

On the day that Gladys died, my sisters asked me if I could write a eulogy. Still in shock over my mother's sudden passing, all I could say was, "Do I have to read it?" But even as we spoke, my voice still trembling from the unreality of the moment, my mother's many lives began to come back to me. And later that day as I ran my laps around the park in Marion, South Carolina, I suddenly realized...that no matter what I wrote, my mother, by her very nature, would find something good in it. Soon, all of the anxiety, all of the fear, and even some of the grief began to leave me as I wrote swiftly on yellow legal pads about my mother's wonderful life. And so, with every mother's natural gift — that God-given ability to make it all better — my mother, in her calm, reassuring voice, had once again put my mind at ease.

2003

Allan Lockyer at the camp - 1975

Linda Lockyer at the camp - 1975

"The Willows", Steuben 1967

Hallie 1988

BACK TO THE LAND: A FATHERS' DAY STORY

In 1964, the year The Beatles first came to America, I was in the eighth grade at Millburn Junior High School in New Jersey. My father was 46 then. And five, often six days a week, he drove through heavy traffic to a General Motors ball bearing plant where he had worked for 29 years, starting as a floor sweeper when he was 17. In 1964, he was a shop foreman.

When the plant had an open house, my father brought me to the "shop" to see where he worked. I suspect he also wanted to show off his son to the men on the line. I remember us walking through a long, dimly lit tunnel, where my father said one of his machinists practiced running sprints during his breaks; then we emerged on the shop floor. The noise! It was deafening. I don't know how my father stood it. And for so many years. Perhaps this was why he enjoyed listening to classical music so much. He could play the piano by ear. My father was on his feet all day. And in the summer he'd come home from the plant, plop down in his easy chair, put his feet up on his hassock and say, "Boy, it was hot in that shop today! It must have been a hundred." Because he was a foreman, my father was expected to wear a white shirt and tie every day. No wonder he always encouraged me to become a teacher.

Four years earlier, my parents had bought an old Cape Cod farmhouse and some land in Steuben. It was here that we spent our precious few weeks of vacation each summer. My parents subscribed to *Down East* magazine; they read books by Mary Ellen Chase, Ruth Moore, and Louise Dickinson Rich; and they talked about Maine all the time. My father always spoke wistfully about retiring there some day.

That very same year, over on Long Island, New York, another Maine story was beginning to unfold. It was told to me by my friend Josh, whose family also vacationed in Maine. Josh and I are the same age. He grew up in a middle-class neighborhood in Amityville.

But in 1964, Josh's life changed dramatically. His father, who was then 45, managed an engine-rebuilding plant in Brooklyn. He'd been driving back and forth from Brooklyn about 12 years.

"My father would spend three and a half to four hours a day in traffic," Josh explained. "He was kind of fed up with the rat race, and he just came home one day — I think it was in January — and said he quit. And everybody was like, 'Wow! What's gonna happen?' So my parents decided we were either gonna move to Alaska or Maine.

"They had my aunt come and take care of my brother, sister, and me. Then my parents went up to Maine, cruised around, bought a piece of property, came back and packed us up, and we moved to Flanders Pond in East Sullivan. The woman they bought the land from owned a camp there.

"It was quite a contrast for me. In Amityville, they had just built a brand-new junior high school — a big, million-dollar complex with sliding glass doors and everything — to Sullivan Grammar School — 12 kids in the seventh grade; 14 in the eighth."

And Josh, with his thick wavy brown hair, his dark flashing eyes, and his love of women, would have fit in very nicely at that large suburban junior high in Amityville. He said, "Yeah, everybody back on Long Island thought we were nuts. I know it was a big step, because when we moved into that old camp on Flanders Pond — it was about 16 by 24 — there was no running water, no electricity. The pond was about 100 feet away, and we chopped three feet of ice out and lugged water up. We had a galvanized tub. We'd boil water on the woodstove and take a bath."

I knew that Josh and his family had eventually built a log house on the land they had bought in Gouldsboro, so I just assumed his father had carpentry skills or perhaps a knowledge of architecture. I also assumed he had been contemplating such a move for many years and had come to Maine with the resources needed to carry out his plan. But Josh said, "No, Geez, no. He called my cousin up, and her husband was a carpenter and builder in Vermont. And they came for the weekend; and Saturday morning, they get up, and this guy said to my father, 'Well, what do you want?' And my father said, 'Four walls and a roof.'"

They had moved to Gouldsboro during blackfly season — all five of them sleeping in a tent. With a family to feed and a Long Island mortgage, Josh's parents hadn't been able to put much money aside. The sale of their Long Island home had enabled them to buy the land in Gouldsboro, but the move to Maine, and then the winter of unemployment, had consumed most of their nest egg. They were nearly broke. And Maine summers are awfully short. They needed a house in a hurry, so they began felling trees.

"It was basically chopped out of the woods," Josh continued. "And it was put up green. It's got character. It was just logs...stood upright. It worked.

"That first winter...Geez...We had four walls and a roof all right, but that was it. We had an old pot burner. The walls were one-inch pine boards with no insulation. The logs on the outside were the upright face. It wasn't solid logs; it was basically a lean-to. Then, 12 feet back, the logs were a little shorter. And then on the back wall, the logs were eight feet and they were connected. They were like eight feet apart — a frame of spruce logs.

"My father had an old '51 Woody wagon. And he'd go back and forth to Ellsworth. He'd go to the mill on the back road there at Washington Junction. He'd take a fifth of whiskey, and the guy would give him like a whole carload of reject boards. And that's what we made the walls out of. We sheathed it with that, but it wasn't tongue and groove. They were square-end boards. And because they were rejects, the edges weren't straight. You couldn't butt them together. Then we laid logs for the rafters and we boarded it all up.

"And we froze! We froze! I remember, I couldn't wait to get on the school bus. I would kick the kid out of the seat near the heater: 'Get out of there; that's my seat!'

"I remember comin' down from the sleeping loft in the morning, and the orange juice was frozen in the glass on the table. It would be 14 below outside, and it was like 26 degrees inside the house. It was like: 'Mom, you got an ice pick so I can drink my juice?'

"And because it wasn't tongue and groove, and there were those gaps between the boards, we taped it from the inside with duct tape. So all around the inside of the house were these seams with that gray duct tape on them. And I'm sittin' at the table; and it was blowin' a storm; and the snow was comin' in through the cracks between the boards, and it would hit that duct tape and there was some warmth inside, so the snow would melt, and the water would lift the duct tape and make it unglue.

"And I was sittin' there eatin', and I had a hat on, and a jacket and mittens, and the snow was comin' in and hittin' me in the back of the ears. 'Cause the tape — it just moves down the wall, and all of a sudden the snow's comin' in — right through the side of the wall! Oh, we loved it! We kids thought it was great!

"The reality was...we thought it was hard. And it was hard, but you didn't think about it. And we ate. There was food on the table. There was a lot of beans and macaroni and cheese. Times were hard. But there was a closeness, and I think the thing I got out of it was I could survive anything. I could do anything.

"It was tough. You could complain, but it wouldn't do any good. They weren't gonna move back to Long Island."

That first winter in Gouldsboro, Josh's father cut pulpwood, while his mother tried to make a home for the family in that frigid lean-to. Josh said, "That first Christmas — I remember my father goin' down to see the local pulpwood dealer and askin' him if he'd come over and scale the wood so they could buy Christmas presents. There was an old guy that lived down the shore. He needed a job, so my father and him got together and they cut wood off the property.

"My father was 45 then. And when I look back on it now, it was a big step for him to have taken at that age. But you know, his whole life, all he wanted to do was to work for himself. And he went through two bankruptcies before he ever got to Maine. And he almost went through a third one here. He had a rental business that folded. I mean, my father — you know the old joke; it was like, the old man, if he started something, he'd go order the Cadillac first thing — before the business was off the ground. 'The first thing we need to do is order the Cadillac.' Geez, what an optimist he was!

"He was real good with other people's money. He could make you money, but if you took the exact same situation and gave it to him and he owned it, he'd just go right berserk."

Josh's mother had been brought up in a very stable, conservative Roman Catholic family on Long Island. Her father had worked for the same company for many years. And her parents didn't want her going out with Josh's father. Josh said, "Yep. She was a good Catholic girl. And my father just said, 'Either you're with me or you're not.' That's one bit of advice my father always gave me. He said if you call a woman and ask her for a date and she says she has to wash her hair, don't go back. If her hair is more important than you, you know you've got the wrong one."

So Josh's parents had eloped. And during the first two years of their marriage, they moved 19 times. They had a little Scotty travel trailer. But in spite of all the uncertainty, they got along well together. "They were Ward and June Cleaver," Josh insisted. "If they ever did argue, we never heard it. I think she kept a lot in her. She worried a lot about money. Down in Amityville things were more stable. He eventually got that job in the engine-rebuilding plant and stayed with it about 12 years."

After that first hard winter in Gouldsboro, things got better for Josh and his family. They insulated the house, and covered the outside with slabwood siding. But life would continue to be frustrating for Josh's father.

"My father drove a truck that summer," Josh continued. "Then he tried worm-digging. Then he cut pulpwood again. Then he was a caretaker; he sold metal buildings; he sold Volkswagens in Bangor, and then he sold them in Ellsworth. And then he sold wood splitters; and then he sold mopeds on the road. He sold chain saws on the road; and he sold televisions on the road too. Geez, he did good! Good salesman!

"I know that his whole life he struggled to try to work for himself, and he bounced in and out. I've seen times when he had to go back to work for somebody else. It was tough. He'd do good; he'd start to get ahead, and then it was like, 'Let's go order the Cadillac!' He knew it wasn't his money — it was the bank's — but he'd get caught up in it, and he'd think he could buy anything. He was the eternal optimist. All he ever wanted to do was work for himself — but he never succeeded."

Josh's father lived in the house that he had built until he died. He was 64 when he died of a heart attack.

"We were all real positive," Josh said. "It wasn't like a real bummer time. And he died just like that, and he smoked three packs a day. It's just what he would have wanted — he checked out quick.

"We cremated my father and spewed 'im off the end of Schoodic Point. That's what he wanted. Like for Fathers' Day, or something like that, he always said, 'I don't want anybody comin' to no cemetery.' Well, I go to Schoodic Point."

In July of 1966, on the very last night of our vacation in Maine, my father died suddenly of a massive heart attack. My mother sold our home in New Jersey later that summer, and we moved up to the old Cape Cod house in Steuben. That fall, I was enrolled in Mrs. Thelma Tracy's 10th-grade homeroom at Sumner Memorial High School in East Sullivan.

So was Josh! We became friends. But I didn't learn the story of how he and his family had come to Maine until 25 years later.

38

MY COLLEGE MENTOR

During the fall and early winter of my senior year of high school, I began writing to colleges and universities for applications and information. It was like a wonderful game. I've always loved getting mail, so I'd write to universities in far-flung, exotic places like Arizona, Arkansas, and Colorado, and they'd send me their glossy brochures. I'd show them to my classmates at Sumner High School, and they'd go, "Yeah right. Like you're really going way out there." Altogether, I wrote to more than 20 colleges and universities — all of them in the South, Southwest, or West.

I had wanted to play college baseball, so I decided to go some place that had a long season. I had no interest in academics. There was no point in my applying to colleges that had rigorous entrance requirements, because I wouldn't have been accepted; my grade point average was about a C-minus. I was not college material. I was also a reluctant traveler. I had never been away from home on my own; had never even slept over at a friend's house. But I had a 350cc Yamaha motorcycle and was curious about places. Maps intrigued me. In the end, I had to force myself to leave home. But I was lucky. I had a mentor. His name was Josh Snowe, and he was from Ashville, Maine.

Josh and I graduated from Sumner High School in 1969. We both went to Southern State College in Magnolia, Arkansas that fall. Actually, there were four of us from Sumner who went — Josh, Wilbur, Zack, and me.

I left Maine a week early because I was making the 1,800 mile trip on my motorcycle. Wilbur went by plane. The first day I saw him on campus, he said, "Geez, Al, ain't it hot!" Didn't he realize the South would be hot? Wilbur and I ran cross country. We were dying of the heat. But Wilbur was also smitten by a girl back home. He dropped out of college after only two months. He married her, of course, then got divorced a few years later.

Josh and Zack rode down in Josh's old Volkswagen. We all went to a reception for incoming freshmen. And when the Dean asked Zack why he had chosen Southern State College, he replied, "Well, I had a friend who had a Volkswagen, and he was going here, so I thought I'd ride down with him." Zack lasted the year. He was frequently drunk, or high on dope. Josh lasted a year too. I never really understood why he went to Arkansas.

"I went there 'cause you were goin' there," Josh later explained. "I wasn't really serious about college to begin with. I think I went down there just because I wasn't sure why I was goin' to college. And then you looked into it, and I remember lookin' through the stuff and sayin', 'Hey, yeah! That's good enough. Sure! Arkansas, great! I'll take a trip!'

"My father was all upset. He couldn't understand it. He kept sayin', 'Why do you want to go to Arkansas?' And I kept sayin', ' 'cause I've never been there. Why not!' And I said, 'Everybody's goin' to the University of Maine — the whole class — everybody's goin' there.' And I think, deep down, I knew I wasn't gonna make it, so I might as well go somewhere and have a good time."

How different my freshman year would have been if Josh had not decided to go to Arkansas! Neither Zack nor Wilbur would ever have gone. I would have been all alone. It was like a part of home had come with me. We were like a little delegation from Maine in that strange and alien Arkansas culture.

When I first arrived on campus, after riding 1,800 miles on my motorcyle, I just wanted to keep on going. The first hour, I just sat on my bike by the athletic field and watched the football team practice. I don't think I had committed myself yet to the idea of staying and actually enrolling. Perhaps I really hadn't thought beyond the trip itself. Maybe, deep down, I too, had no inclination to actually go and then succeed in college. I wasn't a party animal like Josh, but I wasn't exactly a scholar either. After a while, a student wandered over, inspected my bike, then asked me if I was just passing through. I hesitated, then admitted that I was going to be a student there. He asked me which dormitory I had been assigned to, gave me directions, and over I went. I had that anxious, nauseous feeling. I was miserable. I telephoned my mother that evening and told her I didn't think I'd stay.

Josh and Zack arrived the next day. I was a little surprised they actually showed up. My mood lightened. Josh and Zack were much more outgoing than I, and made friends easily. Josh's beat up old Volkswagen, with its Maine license plates, and peace signs painted all over it, was a curiosity. Josh immediately had an audience; then a following: The news of his arrival seemed to spread across the small campus like wildfire. And suddenly, I became known just by association. "Oh, he's one of those weird guys from Maine. He rode all the way down here on a motorcycle!" "He did? Wow!" The next time I telephoned my mother, I told her that I might try it for a while.

Josh Snowe, Sumner High School's greatest comedian, with his mischievous brown eyes and unkempt mop of brown hair, had arrived on campus wearing the same worn-out cut-off jeans, the same grubby old clothes he had bummed around Bar Harbor in all summer. One of the first things I remember him saying was, "Look how straight everyone is!" We were all taken aback. Arkansas was nothing like Maine. Most of the guys on campus had neatly trimmed hair; many wore dress slacks and wing-tipped shoes. And this was the year of the Woodstock Music Festival! But deep down in the heart of the Bible Belt, Arkansas was perhaps five or ten years behind the rest of the country. Here in Magnolia, they were still preoccupied with beauty contests, football, bream fishing, frog jig-ging, rodeo riding, squirrel hunting, and religion. The ABS (Association of Baptist Students) was the largest organization on campus. There were hardly any blacks on campus yet, but there were still plenty of Southern rednecks, and none of them had ever seen anyone like Josh, or his baby blue Volkswagen.

"Old Blue...that was a classic," Josh recalled. "I bought that car for a hundred dollars. It was my first car. Instead of goin' to trigonometry, I did the body work in the shop at Sumner. And Mr. Perry said, 'Well, I can't flunk you, 'cause you weren't here. So I gave you an incomplete.'

"I had done all the body work and I painted it up baby blue, and she was lookin' good. Then it popped out of gear, rolled down an embank-ment, and smashed on the rocks at Frenchman Bay. It bent the crankshaft. That was about three days before Zack and I were to leave for Arkansas. So I called up Bud Norton, and I said, 'Bud, you got an engine that'll fit this car?' And he said, 'Yes—sa, Mr. Man. I got one right here. Fifty bucks...she's all yours. Don't know if she's a good engine or not.'

"So we yanked that old engine out and slapped that other engine in. Well, Zack and I loaded that son-of-a-gun up, and we burned a quart of oil every hundred miles. We got to the point where we were burning fifty weight racing oil.

"It was a great adventure. We knew we were runnin' with a weak engine. You almost had to peddle up hills. So we got some shoe polish out and painted ARKANSAS OR BUST on it, and painted it up with peace signs. People went by and beeped.

"We stopped at Hot Springs, Arkansas on the way down and met these two nurses. We got the guy at the motel to buy a fifth of whiskey for us, and we were right at it, trying to get those nurses drunk. We stayed there a couple of days before we went on to college. We made it!

"When I finally went to sell that car...I remember makin' a sign. I found this thing in a magazine that read: FOUR OUT OF FIVE UNWED MOTHERS. And I put the sign on there so it read: FOUR OUT OF FIVE UNWED MOTHERS DEFINITELY APPROVE OF THIS CAR! I sold it for a hundred bucks. I let her go."

That unbelievable year in Arkansas, Josh seemed to go everywhere, and do everything, except study. Women, more than anything else, were foremost on his mind. At first, he dated several different girls; then he settled on a tall, soft, pouting blonde, who was very pretty, but seemed like the antithesis of him. This was especially rankling to the guys in the dorm, who couldn't understand why such an attractive girl like Gloria would go out with such a bum like Josh.

He also did more than his share of drinking; and I remember that the guys in the dorm, especially the good ol' boys who hailed from podunk places like Hatfield, Homer, Hope, and Horatio, looked up to him. He was a strange sort of role model, a bad influence on straight-laced Arkansas country boys at a time when the rest of the nation seemed intent on "letting it all hang out."

Josh showed them the way. I'd find him drunk at the oddest hours of the day. He'd been up all night, pondering his future; agonizing over whether he should stay in college. For what? I'd encounter him out front of the dorm in the early afternoon, drunk; he and a guy we'd nicknamed Slip Mahoney, their arms around each other — I guess, to keep from falling down — singing this ridiculous song.

"I never really intended to tick anybody off at that college," Josh explained. "You know, people got upset with you real easy if you were just having a good time. And I really was havin' a good time!"

Josh and I went to New Orleans on my motorcycle that Thanksgiving. We spent the first night at a Salvation Army in Alexandria, Louisiana. I remember lying on a cot in a dingy ward where several grizzled old derelicts kept belching and passing gas, and wondering what I was doing there. They fed us grits and eggs in the morning, and before we stepped out into the pouring rain and climbed aboard my Yamaha, the elderly gentleman who ran the place said, "Wait just a minute." He disappeared briefly, then returned holding in his hands a big, old canvas trenchcoat — the sort of raincoat some stodgy Englishman might have worn in one of those old 1930s Scotland Yard detective movies. I had on a rain slicker, but Josh was pleased as punch to get that trenchcoat. And that winter, he wore it on campus, with a pith helmet he'd bought at the local Army-Navy store, and a pair of aviator sunglasses.

We stayed the following night at a YMCA in New Orleans that turned out to be overrun with gay men. The next day, we hung out on the French Quarter, then retreated across the long Lake Ponchartrain Causeway in a howling rainstorm that just about blew us and the Yamaha into the water. We found a campground, and nearly froze to death — or, at least I did — that night. I remember getting up in the wee hours of the morning, going into the Men's Room, and hudding around the little gas space heater. As usual, Josh awoke that morning just as fresh and rested as could be. Nothing ever fazed him.

The last night of our journey, we stayed in a cabin at a state park in central Louisiana. We drank Jax beer, and Josh talked for hours about women, especially Gloria, the long-legged blonde who seemed to be falling in love with him.

A couple of months later, one Thursday night in the dead of winter, Josh and I started talking about going to Mexico. I had been down there on the Yamaha a month earlier visiting a friend from our dorm who lived in the Rio Grande Valley. Josh seemed intrigued. He had just gotten his income tax money. We were hanging out in his dorm room — Josh, me, the guy from south Texas, and several of the guys from Arkansas — bantering back and forth about the Mexican border. I could tell Josh was getting the itch. There was only one problem: he had a big math test in the morning, the only test besides the final exam, he would have in that class. Josh said, "Yeah, my Algebra professor warned us; he said, 'If you're not here for that test, you're all done.'"

The conversation kept building; all of a sudden, it was like a dare. There were all these Arkansas boys, kind of hovering over us, or lurking outside the door, listening, waiting to see if we were really gonna go to Mexico. Finally, around two o'clock in the morning, Josh said, "That's it; you want to see something really crazy? Watch this! We're goin'!" I can still remember Josh saying, as we rode into Louisiana, "I can't believe I'm doing this. I can't believe I'm doing this!"

Josh and I came roaring back on campus Sunday night wearing fringe-leather jackets, the kind that Dennis Hopper wore in the celebrated 1969 film *Easy Rider*. Those guys in the dorm from podunk Arkansas couldn't believe it!

But that wasn't quite the end of the trip for Josh. "I went to math class. And we get into class and sit down, and the first thing out of my professor's mouth is: 'I need to see Mr. Snowe in my office right after this class.'

"He didn't know where I'd been or what had happened. I just said, 'Well, I had a chance to go to Mexico. And I'm from Maine. And I figured that in my lifetime, I'd probably never, ever get another chance to go to Mexico. So I went.'

"He said, 'Well, I guess if I was in your shoes I would have done the same thing.' He says, 'Okay, you can take that test tomorrow.' And when we started that class, the guy said there was absolutely no make-up tests.

"I think I flunked it. You know...what's the difference?"

Josh dropped out of college that spring and returned to Maine. I rode my motorcycle back down to Arkansas my sophomore year, but college would never be the same. It's a good thing...I eventually settled into my studies and managed to earn a degree.

Josh spent his first summer back in Maine over in Bar Harbor, where he got a job washing dishes. He also met a girl named Paige whom he was "head over heels over." "Yeah, I knew I was in a lot deeper than she was," Josh said. "But finally, near the end of the summer, I talked Paige into moving in with me. And then, a few days after she'd moved in, I'm coming out of the restaurant, walking across the street, and I hear, 'Josh...Jo-ah-sh!' in that soft, trembling, whiney voice. I turned around! And it was like, 'OH GEEZ! HOW DID YOU FIND ME!' And I said, 'GLORIA!'"

39

SLEEPING WITH SPUDS

Every old truck, rotting and rusting away, somewhere deep in the Maine woods, has a history. Buried forever in its chassis lies a story about the people who once owned it; about the places it's been; about the lives it's touched. The old truck may be resting in peace with weeds growing out of its sides and mice nesting in its interior, but at one time it was probably the center of someone's life. It might have been their livelihood, maybe even their home. If only we could unlock the mysteries buried in the souls of dead trucks.

I know the story of one such truck. It belonged to a friend of mine named Josh Snowe. He was nearly broke that autumn many years ago. He shouldn't have been; it was September, and he had just finished harvesting his blueberry lease. But it had been a bad year; frost had returned late and burned many of the blossoms. And then the drought had come. Old-timers said it was the driest year anyone around Cherryfield, Maine, could remember. The berries were spotty and small. They were hardly worth the bother. Josh barely made enough money to pay his bills, let alone save any for winter.

Shortly before blueberry season, Josh had bought an old truck to haul his berries. He thought he had gotten a good deal, but soon realized it burned and leaked oil. "The motor was blown," Josh explained. "The engine parts cost me nine hundred. But to have it done in a machine shop would have cost me sixteen hundred. I prob'ly should'a had it bored, and put new pistons in it. I just had it honed."

He had no prospects for work...nothin' goin' on, as Josh put it. So he borrowed the money for the parts, then worked day and night rebuilding the truck. Maybe he could use it to haul something. But what?

"I remember seein' this guy on the road the previous fall," Josh said. "I'd see him in Machias one week, Ellsworth another. He was sellin' spuds. He had a hand-made sign on a piece of poster board: AROOST-OOK POTATOES $7 FOR 50 POUNDS!...and he was sellin' 'em on the side of the road. So I said, Geez, I can do that."

Josh Snowe was a rugged, good-looking guy with thick wavy brown hair and sparkling brown eyes who could charm the women like no man I've ever known. He was a natural-born salesman; he was destined to make a killing.

The potato idea came to Josh shortly before his thirtieth birthday. He had an ingenious plan; his optimism was boundless. Josh's girlfriend knew an artist — a struggling artist — a young woman in Milbridge who, with her husband, were just starting out. It is Josh's nature to want to help people. That's just the way he is. He once helped me, an extremely shy and reclusive person, meet my future wife. So he said, "Let's have a sign made up: NEW BORN POTATOES." He told the young artist what the concept was. "I want a four by eight foot sheet, and I want NEW BORN POTATOES across the top. I want a potato in a baby carriage with a bonnet on it, and a thumb stuck in its mouth, peeking out from inside the carriage — a wicker carriage."

On the day of his thirtieth birthday, an excited Josh went back to the artist's studio to pick up his sign.

"It's eighteen hundred dollars," the artist nervously said.

"What! Geez! You're kidding!" Josh couldn't believe it. They hadn't discussed a price. After all, he was doing her a favor; helping her out. He expected it would be a few hundred dollars, more or less.

She said, "You're going to make a lot of money." She began to pull on the skin of her pale thin neck. She looked down at the floor, determined to go through with this. The young artist, who had earlier seemed almost pretty to Josh, had suddenly been transformed into a shrew. She had long, lanky brown hair and the droopy mouth of a heavy smoker. There were dark circles under her milky gray-blue eyes. Her dress, mannerisms, and speech seemed contrived; they hinted of an imposter trying to play out a role, perhaps that of a would-be hippie. But she was ten years too late. Josh described her simply as "one of them organics."

He said, "Apparently, she and her husband got to talking about it, and he had his own truck. They stole my idea. It was either buy it or leave it. So I left it. She and her husband threw the sign in their truck and took off for Aroostook County to buy potatoes. I was crushed. I was absolutely devastated that anyone could be so low. That was my thirtieth birthday. I was in tears.

"But one of the old guys I met sellin' on the road said, 'No, you don't want good signs. People will think you're doin' too good. No. You just want to put it up with ol' magic marker.'"

And that's what he did. Josh drove up to Aroostook County, where he bought potatoes for $3.50 for a 50-pound bag. He figured he could get $7 for a bag down on the coast.

"I took off and I smoked 'er down to Camden," Josh explained. "I got there about noon and this guy let me set up at his gas station on a busy corner. And I sat there. I had seven dollars on the sign and nothing's happening. Well, there's more than one way to get a customer. I tried six. Nothin'. I put five dollars on 'em; and then I started selling potatoes."

It seemed that five dollars was the magic number that fall. Josh would sell a load, then return to Aroostook for another. He would go to Camden one week, Machias the next, then up to Bangor, down to Ellsworth; he was always looking for that perfect roadside spot.

Stacked carefully, the old truck could carry 300 bags. After Josh sold the first tier of 50 bags, he'd rearrange the second tier so as to hollow out a little pocket just large enough to hold his sleeping bag. The truck had an old plywood box with a piece of canvas over the back end but no top. Josh said, "I can remember one rain storm; man, it was comin' down cats and dogs, and me in the back with them potatoes, savin' a dollar 'cause I couldn't afford a motel. At a buck-fifty a bag, that's only four-hundred and fifty for the whole load. Then food and gas, and then the truck breaks down. I kept one step ahead of the truck. If I didn't run it, it wouldn't break down. But as long as I was runnin' the truck it was needing stuff."

He rebuilt the front end, did the kingpins, and replaced the tires. Then he noticed that it was beginning to use a little oil. Meanwhile, the leaves began to turn. The dark green of late summer gave way to splashes of color — red, orange, golden-yellow. The days were brilliantly clear; the nights turned chilly, and then really cold; the rains came back. Like a mole, Josh burrowed deeper into the potato sacks. He said, "Yeah, they had water beds. Well, I thought spud beds would go. Those lumps really would help your back, you know. And those 50-pound sacks — luggin' 'em every day — geez."

There were countless cold rainy solitary nights, when he'd lie amongst the potatoes, zipped up tightly in his sleeping bag, pondering his next move. Where should I go next? Down to Portland? Over to Augusta? Should I leave this spot? It's not goin' too good. What's my next move? Where's my next spot?

He'd roll into a town, size it up, then begin asking questions. Who owns this property? Can I get permission to sell potatoes from this spot? Sometimes he'd have to trade 300 pounds of potatoes for permission to use a site for the day.

"I met all kinds of people," Josh said. "Sometimes they'd come up to me, buy some potatoes and say something like: 'I'd rather buy potatoes from a guy like you...out here trying to make a living — you're not on welfare.' Yeah, a lot of people would be embarrassed or would feel funny about sellin' on the road. I learned there's nothin' to feel embarrassed about if you've got to pay your bills. I wasn't gettin' welfare; I wasn't running drugs; I was just trying to make a living. At the time, it was the only thing I could think of doing with that truck."

Josh was selling spuds on High Street in Ellsworth one September day when a middle-aged man pulled in and said, "God, those sure are good-looking potatoes! Man, you ought to come out to Vermont. You'd make a killing out there! Oh, yeah. Geez, my brother-in-law, he's got a restaurant right in Brattleboro, Vermont. You can come right out there and set up right on the premises. No problem. Here...here's the telephone number...you give us a call."

As the weeks wore on, Josh began to think more and more about this chance encounter. Was the guy on the level? What reason would he have to lie? Josh began to fantasize — Yeah, Brattleboro, Vermont...we've never seen a spud. They're lacking potatoes out there. Yeah, they're a potato-hungry crowd. And the stores are empty!

It was all just a dream, a late-night fantasy that recurred with greater frequency as the nights got colder and the rains persisted. And then the dreaming abruptly stopped. "It was near the end of October," Josh explained. "I'd kinda gotten tired of the run; I'd made all my stops and decided I was gonna run for Brattleboro. I said, I know it's the land of opportunity. Seven dollars a bag! Big money, mama, big money! Order the Cadillac!"

He went with a full load on board. And with his engine burning oil, and getting only about four or five miles to the gallon, his money was dwindling fast.

Josh said, "I took the interstate all the way down through Maine. 'Cause you get her out on the highway, you could get her up to sixty and the tires heat up and she'll start singin' — wum, wum, wum, wum, wum. Well, I was in the truckin' world then. Eatin' at Dysart's Truck Stop; wave to the boys; ask 'em if the scales are open. All this time I was illegal too, because I never had a Class II driver's license."

Brattleboro is in the southern part of Vermont, so Josh cut across New Hampshire on Route 4.

"Let me tell ya', I thought I was in some of them Berkshires goin' out there. I don't know as I got as low as first gear, but I was in second quite a few times...in low range...wum, wum, wum, wum...wum, wum...wum, wum...doin' about three-miles-an-hour, crawlin' up over them hills. But seven dollars a bag...it's the big one, mama! I can see it now!"

He drove all night and arrived in Brattleboro around eleven in the morning.

"I'm pullin' in, and it's like the pot of gold. Here it is! I'm here! I've made it, and I've got 300 bags on board!"

Josh had telephoned the restaurant in Brattleboro before he left Maine. And sure, they didn't mind if he used their parking lot. But when he arrived, he learned he needed a sales permit. He'd have to go down to the Town Hall to get one, so he maneuvered the big truck in the downtown traffic and parked at a nearby gas station. Josh had less than a dollar. The clerk at the Town Hall said, "That's five dollars."

"Oh geez."

He went back to the gas station, found the owner and said, "Geez, you wouldn't want to buy a bag of potatoes? That permit's five dollars and I ain't got five dollars."

"Sure, I'll take one."

"Great! I'm gonna get seven for these, but you can have it for five bucks."

So Josh got his permit, went back to the restaurant, and set up his operation. Seven dollars a bag, this was what he'd been waiting for all season. But something was wrong. The location couldn't have been better. Cars pulled in and out of the restaurant all afternoon. It was busy. Customers came by, glanced at his sign and went on. By late afternoon, he'd only sold a half dozen or so bags. "I'm sittin' there and nothin's happening," Josh said. "So I got a little restless and strolled out to the street to stretch my legs. I look down the street and I see this big Shaw's Supermarket. The sun was goin' down, so I put up my signs and cruised over to Shaw's. OH GEEZ! GEEZ! GEEEEZ! They were sellin' 50-pound bags of spuds for four-seventy-nine! Four-seventy-nine!"

Josh drove up to the Holiday Inn. He didn't dare spend the money for a room, but they had a big dirt parking lot for trucks, and they let him park there for the night. "And it poured. It came down in cats and dogs, and I was sleeping with them spuds, and around two o'clock in the morning these drunk guys are out there in the parking lot. It's all mud now. They're in this beat-up old car, drunk right out of their minds, revving the engine and cuttin' doughnuts in the mud. And I'm like peeking out from behind my tent goin', what the...is goin' on? And it is pouring! I finally said, no, I've had enough of this. I got up next morning and smoked her out of there."

Josh had made enough money for some gasoline, but not enough to get him home. By eleven the next morning, he had reached the Dover, New Hampshire circle. He said, "I see this circle, and I see some activity on this little pull-out off the circle. So I pulled in and set up my signs...see if I can't sell a few spuds. I'm almost out of gas...and money. And I'm standin' there...standing' there...people goin' by, nothin' goin' on. And this guy pulls in, and he's got a van and a little hot dog wagon behind it. He jumps out, pops the tent up on the hotdog stand, opens up the van, and he's got buckets of flowers in there. And then three or four cars pull in. So he starts sellin' everybody flowers. Then he unhooks the hotdog wagon, parks it, and people just start pullin' in, one right after the other, and they're buyin' flowers off him, and he's pumping hotdogs left and right. This guy is like he's on stage; he's talkin' and he's juggling hot-dogs; he's been there a long time, everybody knows him.

"And I'm standin' there with my spuds, watching all this. We must be doing something wrong. This spud business just ain't all it's cracked up to be. I sold two bags."

Josh stayed the afternoon, then finally gave up. He had enough gas money to get to Augusta, where he spent the night. "It was raining cats and dogs again," Josh explained. "It must have been nearly midnight, and I parked in that lot where Burger King is, and crawled in with my spuds. I was beat. I still had most of my load, but I was in striking distance of home."

In the morning the sun was shining. There's no place like Maine, Josh thought. He went across the street to the Augusta Armory and discovered they were having a home show. His luck had turned. He said, "I'd had enough. I put four-fifty on them suckers! I sold the whole load in about four hours! Man, I was luggin' 'em just as fast as I could go. Old ladies: 'I'll take six bags. Could you lug them to my car?' 'Yes, ma'am.'

"Geez, if you'll take six bags, I'll peel 'em for ya'! The last bag went out and I jumped in the truck and smoked her home. That was the end of it. I never ran another spud."

40

POTATOES, MUSTARD AND BEER

What can a young man from Maine do when he's out of work, out of money and autumn has arrived? If he's adventurous like my friend Josh, he might head south to Florida. Once in Florida, the only reference he'll need is "Maine."

"But first we had to have some money to get there," Josh explained. "I borrowed a hundred bucks from Zack. Then Zack, Randy and me...we go to Randy's house in South Paris, Maine. We go over to Mr. Peterson's farm and he hires us, and we're getting 50 cents a bushel for apple pickin'. I guess we picked for like two weeks. It's like takin' 50 pounds and strappin' it on your shoulders; then go climb a ladder and stay on that ladder all day with 50 pounds strapped to your back. Geez! It was like somebody beat me with a hammer at the end of the day.

"Well, we worked and we played. We drank beer and we watched the World Series and we chased women. By the time I paid back Zack his hundred dollars and we left for Florida, I had less than a hundred bucks.

"We had Randy's old Volkswagen Beetle. And we get to New York. Now Randy's barely been off the farm. He was Finnish; big bear of a guy, real easy goin', like Gentle Ben. Randy's been to Winter Harbor. That was his big trip. So we get to my sister's house on Long Island. Randy had never been in to the city, so we decided it was very important for him to go in and have a hot dog. 'Cause New York City's famous for its hot dogs. That was the whole thing. We were goin' to find one of them street vendors so he could have a hot dog.

"So we take off in Randy's Volkswagen. We get across the bridge and we're cruisin' around Manhattan and it's like, Park Avenue! Broadway! We stopped and we had the hot dog.

"So we get the hot dog and we're ready to smoke 'er out of there. We take off and we're goin' under the Brooklyn Bridge, then all of a sudden the generator's throwin' sparks. We were gonna catch on fire! So we stop the engine. She's overheated.

"He cranks it over and the bearings are gone on the generator. So I said, 'Randy, this thing's just totally blown...we can't go anywhere...we can't do nothin'.' And it's like, where are we? Cars are goin' overhead. There's a tunnel ahead. We get the tools out and I say, 'Here's what we'll do. We'll take the fan belt off and it won't turn the generator. But if it doesn't turn the generator, it won't cool the engine. But if we let the engine cool down, we'll have a certain amount of time we can run this car before she heats up.'

"So we let it cool down. We start it up. I say, 'Goose 'er, let's go!' We made it through the tunnel, just got through, and we shut it off. It's like that all the way to my sister's — three or four miles, then shut if off — six hours to go 50 miles.

"We went to a junkyard and got a generator. Then we drove straight through to Fort Lauderdale, watched the sun come up on the beach and said, 'No, we're headed for Key West.' Got down to Key West, checked it out and said, 'No, this doesn't look like where it's gonna happen 'cause we're runnin' out of money.'

"So we headed back to Fort Lauderdale. A friend of mine from Maine was working at a marina there. He said he could help us find jobs. So there's three of us in that Volkswagen, plus all of our gear. It was packed so high that we put the poles for the tent underneath the back seat. And I'm sittin' in the back seat, and all of a sudden I think I smell smoke. I'm sniffin' and sniffin', and we're on that long causeway across the Keys where there's no place to pull off. I said, 'Randy! Geez! Christ! We're on fire!' And he just stops in the middle of the highway. Everybody jumps out. We rip all of the stuff out of the back...throwin' it all over the road. And those metal tent poles had bounced down and shorted on to the battery. It caught the coarse, horsehair stuffing beneath the seat on fire. And the only fire extinguisher we had was a beer. So I shook the beer up and popped the top and put the fire out. We put the fire out with a Budweiser!

"So we get everything back in the Volkswagen and we're headed to Fort Lauderdale. What we didn't realize was...when we shorted out the battery, it had burnt out the generator we had just put in. So now we're drivin' along and the lights go out. Well, I arrived in Fort Lauderdale with five bucks. I got a haircut, washed my clothes at a laundromat, went out and begged for a job.

"I got a job at the marina where my friend from Maine worked. They put Randy as the cleanup guy and me in the parts room. Zack got a job down the beach, cookin' at a place called The Fork and You.

"We all pooled our money and scraped enough to rent an apartment. The landlord gave us a little time to come up with the first month, last month and security deposit. So we bought 10 pounds of potatoes, Randy and me, and was having potatoes and mustard and beer for supper. We couldn't afford butter but they had cheap beer down there. We'd finally get our paycheck and it was all goin' to catch up on this rent deal. But first, we'd go to this Sweden House, where it was all you could eat. On Saturday, we'd just barrel down there. People'd go, 'Geez, those guys can eat!' Cripes, it was the only meal we'd eaten all week except potatoes, mustard and beer.

"So I started in the parts room of this big marina and the parts guy said to me, 'I can't keep any half decent kid in here.' What happens...one of these yacht captains comes in and offers you a better paying job. The parts guy goes, 'Where you from? Maine? Of all the places to be from...I can't keep anybody from Maine.' What it is...Maine is established as a state that produces honest, hardworking people. And the rich people down there; that's old money; they're looking for honest, hardworking caretakers. The guy that sold the uniforms to the boats; he could peddle you just like that! 'You're from Maine? I can have you on a yacht.' Just like that. The only reference I needed was Maine.

"So this parts guy knew I wasn't gonna last. Because I'm workin' the parts counter, and every captain is coming there to get parts for his boat. You get chatty with them...all of a sudden one of them offers you a job on the boat. After a month or so, I'd already had several little offers. Then the captain of the Falcon showed up. She was the biggest yacht in the marina and the whole crew was from Maine.

"Randy and I were making minimum wage. The captain goes, 'I've got a cook's job and a steward's job. You interested?' He offered us fifteen-hundred a month to start. Plus, you've got everything — food, lodging, uniform, underwear, film for your camera. A guy comes and measures you and they deck you right out — shoes, socks, you name it.

"The boat was owned by Leland Ramsey. He owned several professional sports franchises. He owned two banks. The Falcon was 120 feet or so on the deck. We carried the owner and eight guests. There was a master stateroom, then three more staterooms. They all had these framed pictures of famous people they'd taken out...John Wayne, Julie Andrews, Ernest Borgnine, LBJ and Lady Bird...actors, politicians, you name it.

"The captain gave Randy and me a couple hundred bucks and told us to go buy underwear. It was the only thing the uniform guy didn't bring. He told us to go buy underwear and then go out and have a good steak dinner. It was to let you know you were in a dream world. Everything was gonna be taken care of.

"Well, I was gonna be wearin' whites 'cause I was the cook. Did I buy regular underwear? No, sir. I bought flourescent pink boxer shorts. The captain would come right in there and it would just freak him right out. He'd see that flourescent pink right through the whites. It's like I haven't even started and already I was rockin' the boat.

"So Randy and I went on board. And we're leavin' on a trip...just like that. So I had no chance to practice or nothin'. That first breakfast they wanted bacon. So I took a pound of bacon, threw it on the frying pan and I was fryin' it up. Geez, I didn't know rich people like it flat. They don't want crinkled bacon; it's got to be ironed right out. The captain came in and said, 'Geez! No, geez, you can't do that!' There were set ways of doing things.

"So Randy's the steward and I'm learnin' the ropes, cookin' some decent meals. But the captain is a prima donna. And when things don't go the way he wants them to go, he gets mad and you're supposed to get upset and worry about it. Well, we didn't. I remember, we're goin' to Nassau for the first time. And we're all dancin' in the galley...goin' to funky Nassau, here we go! We're all excited. Never been to Nassau!

"The captain, he'd kind of bait you with money. 'Well, you're gonna go ashore, boys; here's some money.' That's to get you hooked into the system. And I cooked this real nice turkey dinner for this woman on board. She was this hot ticket. Well, she knew we were goin' ashore for the first time...she takes my hand and puts a hundred dollar bill in it! I say, 'Thank you, ma'am!' So we went out howling!

"It was spring break and there must have been a hundred women in this bar and maybe 10 guys! I couldn't believe it. I just kept lookin' around, lookin' around, then 'Want to dance?' 'Yeah!' I met this girl and we danced and I got back to the boat around four o'clock in the morning and I had to get up at five. The captain was steamed. I put in 18 hours that day.

"But I would not cry uncle. We were supposed to have moderated ourselves and be in at a decent hour. Well, this started building a little bit. And soon we did the same thing again. Well, the captain sits down at the breakfast table and he starts ranting! Well, we got through breakfast, and I said, 'All right, you watch this.' We set a candlelight dinner of beans and hot dogs for the crew for lunch! I mean, we had everything...the linens out, the classical music on. It was like, 'You want to mess with us, we'll mess with you!'

"Randy and I didn't exactly get into trouble, but it was kind of like not joining the club. We got along, but it's a clique. It's the captain and the first mate and the second mate; they're in the club and they want you to conform. And we were the free spirits. We were supposed to give a damn. And we didn't. They couldn't understand that.

"Yeah, we had this kid on the crew from Cranberry Island, and he'd never seen caviar before. He said, 'What's that?' I said, 'Oh, that's fish eggs.' He said, 'Oh geez, I like fish eggs.' And he whipped out two slices of bread, dumped about a pound of caviar on there and made a sandwich. That stuff was about 300 bucks for just a little tub! He wolfed down that sandwich and said, 'Geez, that ain't too bad, but I don't know as I could make a meal of it.'

"Yeah, we cruised the Bahamas, then came back and did all the yacht clubs. We did a cocktail party for 150 people in West Palm Beach. They put me in as bartender. Well, I'd never done it; and this old guy — he must have been about 85 — orders a whiskey on the rocks. So I gave him one of these great big tumblers with about one cube of ice and I filled it up with whiskey. He took it and walked off. And the mate says to me, 'What the hell you tryin' to do, kill him?' 'Geez, I don't know. He said he wanted it straight up!'

"Well, spring was coming and Randy and I decided we were all done. We wanted to get back to Maine. But the captain and the mate took us aside and said, 'Do you know what you're doing!' And all of a sudden they're showering you with money. The tips are getting bigger. They're offering you a big raise. It's hard to get honest people. The owner had a toilet seat cover that was filled with money...coins and stuff. He had gold bathroom fixtures. You could have walked off with all kinds of stuff. If you took a hammer and a wrench you could have pawned enough to live on for a couple of years.

"They try to convince you that you've got a good future there; that you don't have to worry about money; that you're gonna be set; that Mr. Ramsey can make anything happen for you. Yeah, old man Ramsey...if he liked you...he'd have a brand new Chevy station wagon on the dock, piece of junk to him, and he'd give it to a crewmember for 500 bucks. 'Here, take it!'

"It's a trade-off. You sell your soul. When the owner's not there, you've got some freedom. But when he's there, you're a servant. If he calls you at two o'clock in the morning, you're gonna get up. The captain can make as much money as a good doctor or lawyer. He had an eighth-grade education. All he is is a caretaker for a rich man's floating property. Captains look for good talent, young guys to bring in; then they flood them with money and they get them hooked into it. None of them would ever admit to themselves that they've been sucked into it, and they ain't got the guts to get out. And somebody that's makin' that kind of money with no education...they're sayin', too, that they can't get out.

"So in the end, the captain took me down in his cabin and said, 'You know, I've never seen Mr. Ramsey take a shine to anybody as quickly as he has to you. Your future's virtually set here.' It went on and on.

"I made the move first. Randy hung on another week. I had bought an old Volkswagen without a starter for 200 bucks. The captain looked at my old VW and said, 'How you gonna make it all the way back to Maine without a starter?' I said, 'I can start it myself on flat ground. I can push it fast enough to jumpstart it. And if it isn't flat, I've got a hill.' He just shook his head. He had a brand new Cadillac. I said, 'If you took off for Maine in your new Cadillac and you got halfway up there and the engine blew, what would you have to do? You'd have to call a wrecker; you'd have to spend a couple of thousand bucks for a new engine. I've got everything I need right in this backpack. And if the motor blows on this Volkswagen, all I've got to do is kick it off to one side of the road, grab my backpack and start hitchhiking, and I'll be home before you!'

"One last memory I have of that boat is of a crystal clear night in the Bahamas. The harbor was real small and we looked like the Queen Mary there. And it was all condos around this harbor. When we pulled in, all the little people would come round and put notes on the boat, saying, 'Would you come for cocktails?' They could say, 'Oh, we had the so and so's over for cocktails.'

"So this night, I was sittin' there on this long, cement dock. And I had walked way down to the end where it was dark and I could look over and see the boat. She was lit up softly. It was after midnight, and I was sitting there with my feet dangling, and the stars were just brilliant. And I just kept lookin' at those stars and all I could think about was Maine."

EPILOGUE

The telephone rang late one evening in November. It was a call from Sullivan, Maine. Word had been passed along the Downeast grapevine from a friend in Steuben, to another friend in Gouldsboro, to my friend in Sullivan, and then to me: my friend, Josh, had suffered a heart attack. He was in Eastern Maine Medical Center. They were putting stents in several of his arteries.

I began to tremble. The Downeast world I had always imagined as rock-solid began to quake beneath me. I telephoned Josh the next day. I tried to be upbeat. "We just got home from the hospital," his wife said. "He's right here. Let me put him on." I was relieved to hear her voice. She had helped him turn his life around in the 1980s and had given him a focus. He had come a long way since his days of selling potatoes on the road. Still, my conversation with Josh was awkward. So reassuring to hear his voice; yet, so unsettling. "At least I had a warning," Josh said. He sounded tired, shaken, but thankful. "My father never got a warning. Neither did yours."

I'm not always comfortable talking long-distance on the telephone. I'm better at writing letters. And our friendship — face to face since Mrs. Thelma Tracey's 10th grade homeroom at Sumner High School —has never seemed quite normal on the telephone.

We are our father's sons. I have no recollection of my father ever speaking into a telephone. Isn't that strange? Surely he must have used the telephone from time to time, but I have no memory of it. Growing up in New Jersey, the lone black telephone in our home was on a stand in the hallway. I have vivid memories of my mother and sisters using it, but never my father. I even remember the number: Drexel 9-4637.

To be nearing 53 is realize life's limitations. Josh, who had eventually settled down and started a successful construction business, was also building a new home when the heart trouble began. He did most of the work on the house himself. Every time we stopped by the past two summers, my wife, Linda, and I had marveled at how much more he'd gotten done. After all, he was at work with his crew all week erecting metal buildings. And he always seemed to have additional jobs lined up. Where did he get his energy? How did he do it? By comparison, my own job seemed like a pushover.

In recent years, Josh had also started writing and publishing his own children's books. Always a creative person, he delighted in writing the stories, then giving occasional readings at local schools. It is something I can imagine him doing more of when he eventually retires from the construction business. Berry Cove Publishing Company is Josh's creation. It only seemed natural that I should approach Josh as a publisher for this book, especially since some of the stories are about his life.

Indeed, Josh and I often wonder what ever became of Gloria, the pretty blond coed who followed him all the way to Maine from Arkansas, the summer after our freshman year of college. "It's over," he'd told her, after she'd shocked him by just showing up one day in Bar Harbor. She was relentless in her hot pursuit. It was as though she'd had a fatal attraction. She refused to leave. She even managed to land a job as a waitress at Jasper's Restaurant in Ellsworth, before finally returning to Arkansas in the fall. She dropped out of college. We never saw her again, but heard through a friend that she had married a preacher.

"You don't need cartilage," a colleague in the Philosophy Department had told me last fall. He had just run the New York City Marathon. "Mine's all gone…football injuries. The quadriceps and the muscles around the knee will grow stronger. You can still run the marathon."

I wanted to believe him. I began to believe him. I increased my long runs to 17 miles through the fall and winter in preparation for the Myrtle Beach Marathon in February. But when race day arrived it was not so much the knee but the weather that gave me trouble. It was humid and very windy, and after we had passed the half-way point the sun came out and the temperature climbed into the 70s.

It had been five years since I had run a marathon—five years since I had raced more than 13 miles. The knee stiffened. I began to feel really weak from dehydration. We were running directly into a strong, south wind along the boulevard. By 23 miles my legs were cramping. I'd run a little farther, cramp, walk a few paces, and start jogging again. The miles seemed endless. Linda was there when I made the final turn towards the finish. I'd been running for 4 hours and 5 minutes. She later said that the crowd had blocked her from seeing the medics slip a wheelchair under me when I crossed the finish line. I had clutched my ribs—my stomach muscles were cramping, along with my calves. I also had a cramp in the back of my neck. I was severely dehydrated, despite all the water and sports drinks I had drunk along the course. The medics hurriedly wheeled me into a triage area under the stadium where dozens of dehydrated runners were being fed glucose intravenously.

I collapsed on a stool. A nurse rushed over to take my blood pressure. A doctor with a clipboard began asking me questions.

"Have you ever run a marathon before?"

"This was my 54th. I've been running since I was 15." He looked surprised. And I thought: It won't be my last one either!

"How old are you?"

"Fifty-two."

"How many miles a week do you run?"

"Fifty." A young boy came over and draped a finisher's medal around my neck.

"I'm okay," I said. "I'm just a little dehydrated. You've got to let me out of here. My wife's gonna be worried about me."

"You're sure you're okay?"

"I'm fine."

I got back on my feet and shuffled slowly, past the cots of exhausted, dehydrated runners. I made my way out through the tunnel into the light of day.

Maine has the highest high school graduation rate in the nation (85.4 % according to the 2000 U.S. Census). Nevertheless, Maine ranks at the very bottom of New England states in the percentages of people over 25 who are college graduates (22.9 %). The standard explanation is that Maine is a poor state. Yet Washington, Maine's eastern-most and poorest county, still ranks above Somerset, Piscataquis, and Aroostook in the percentage of college graduates. And in adjacent Hancock County, where Gouldsboro lies, the percentage of college graduates is nearly twice that of Washington. Do the higher percentages in Hancock and Washington Counties suggest that residents of these eastern coastal counties are more serious about education than their counterparts in northern Maine? Perhaps, but I doubt it. Until recently, many high school graduates in northern Maine could count on well-paying jobs in paper mills and thus forgo college.

To me, these statistics only reinforce what we already know about the coast—that it's an attractive place to live, and that people with college degrees want to live here regardless of the economy. While many transplants are drawn to Hancock because it offers better shopping, more cultural activities, and is less remote than Washington, both counties have immense appeal. I believe that people who have money will continue to buy waterfront property in Maine. It's simply a good investment, especially when stocks are so volatile.

Yet like many camp owners, I fear for the future of Jones Pond. We were all relieved a few years ago when a young couple, both recent graduates of the College of the Atlantic, bought a 100 acre farm with frontage on Jones Pond. Word had it that a Bar Harbor developer offered more than $10,000 dollars above the asking price. But the previous owners did not want the land developed into house lots. They wanted it to remain a farm, which was the intention of the young couple. Good for them! We all hope they can turn it into a productive working farm, something that's not easy to do these days.

Unfortunately, most Maine coastal and lakefront property is sold to the highest bidder. And I often wonder if it is only a matter of time before my childhood fantasy of a rustic camp in the Maine woods will be lost forever.

After a long absence I'm finally home at Jones Pond. Nothing looks the same. The heath behind the camp is gone. North towards Route 1, the land is wide open except for a few scattered trees. A paved road runs alongside our outhouse. My eyes follow it out to Bar Point, where a big, brand new home now stands. Looking out at the pond from the front of our camp, I notice that this new home obscures our view of Bar Point. The house and docking area seem to dominate the whole eastern shoreline of our cove. The pond itself looks shrunken and shallow and muddy, like a dying lake in Mexico, or maybe a mudflat during the outgoing tide. Clumps of brown algae are floating on the surface. It's hard to believe I used to swim here.

Who are these new neighbors of mine? I can hear their voices. They're too close for comfort. They've got kids. How did they get a permit to build there? Everything seems so strange. There's a large garage, shaped like a saltbox barn, with an SUV parked in front. Two teenagers are strapping on life vests, getting ready to ride two bright orange personal watercraft. I keep wondering—how did they ever build a road out to Bar Point? They must have really drained a lot of water out of the pond. At its narrowest point, only about a foot of land had separated Fred's Cove from our cove. I could stand on that narrow neck and cast my line into either cove. I could drag my boat up over the bar from one cove to the next. I had cut a secret path from our property through the bushes out to the narrows. My new neighbor's driveway is where my secret path had been. Looking over into Fred's Cove, I can see several more new houses around the shoreline. What happened to the pickerel grass and the lily pads? The beaver lodge is gone too. I just see driveways and green lawns sloping down to the shallow, muddy water. On the hillside, heading up towards Route 1, the honeysuckle thicket, the stand of pines, the old apple trees, the maples and birches and cedars—they're all gone. So are the four-wheeler trails where I used to walk with Bess.

How did this happen? I'm starting to feel sick. The camp is completely exposed. There's Route 1, this new subdivision, our camp, outhouse, and the shallow muddy pond. It's like a bad dream, where one minute I'm getting out of my wet running clothes after a race; the next minute I'm cowering naked in a crowded shopping mall. What's become of my clothes? I can't find them. What an awful feeling—to be so vulnerable. I've got to find an empty shopping bag. I need something to cover myself with. What if any of my students were to see me?

I should have known this would happen to the camp. It's already happened in northern Maine, where a huge new national park has been carved out of the north woods. The developers have destroyed that whole area. Hollywood money has transformed Piscataquis County into the land of the gated community, where a waitress can make more in tips during the short summer season than a school teacher can earn in a year. It was only a matter of time before it happened here. And all my life, all I've ever really wanted was this camp.

I feel like my neighbors are staring at me. They're going to want me to tear down the outhouse. I just know it. They'll say it's an eyesore. They'll argue that it's driving down property values. It's got to go, along with this old camp. You can't live without electricity or indoor plumbing in a nice neighborhood like this. I don't belong here anymore. My sadness is inconsolable. I can't stand to be here another minute, and suddenly I am not.

I'm sitting cross-legged on the bed. My eyes are open and I'm looking at myself in the mirror of Linda's dresser. I look like I've been to hell and back. It's taking me a while to realize it was only an anxiety dream. It's still March. I've got to get ready for class.

March 2004

References

Beals, Ralph L., Cheran: *A Sierra Tarascan Village.* Westport, CT: Greenwood Press, 1970.

Bode, Carl, Editor, *The Portable Thoreau.* New York: The Viking Press, 1965.

Casey, Edward S., "Between Geography and Philosophy: What Does It Mean to Be in the Place-World?" *Annals of the Association of American Geographers*, Vol. 91, December 2001, pp. 683-693.

Chatwin, Bruce, *Anatomy of Restlessness.* New York: Penguin Books USA Inc., 1996.

Franzen, Jonathan, "Imperial Bedroom," *The New Yorker*, October 12, 1998, pp. 48-53.

Kunhikannan, Palangadan, *A Down East Fishing Community: The Processes of Transformation*, doctoral dissertation, Department of Anthropology, State University of New York at Stony Brook, 1984.

LaFranchi, Howard, "Mexicans' Ancient Tradition of Honoring Their Ancestors," *The Christian Science Monitor*, 20 November 1996: 12.

Lockyer, Allan, *Clamdiggers and Downeast Country Stores: Eastern Maine's Vanishing Culture.* Orono, Maine: Northern Lights Inc., 1993.

Lockyer, Allan, *The Reluctant Traveler: Passage in the Troubled Heartland by Mexican Bus.* Unpublished manuscript.

Lopez, Barry, "The American Geographies," *Orion*, Autumn 1989.

Naipaul, V.S., *A House for Mr. Biswas.* New York: Alfred A. Knopf, Inc., 1961.

Potter, Robert B. and Sally Lloyd-Evans, "Sun, Fun & a Rum Deal: Perspectives on Development in the Commonwealth Caribbean," *Focus*, Winter 1997, p. 22.

Shlaes, Amity, "A Tiger Slumbers in Maine's Northern Woods," *The Downeast Coastal Press*, week of August 28-September 3, 2001.

Stanislawski, Dan, *The Anatomy of Eleven Towns in Michoacán.* Latin American Studies, no. 10. Austin: University of Texas Press, 1950.

Stilgoe, John R., *Alongshore.* New Haven & London: Yale University Press, 1994.

Tuan, Yi Fu, *Escapism.* Baltimore & London: The Johns Hopkins University Press, 1998.

Zurick, David, *Errant Journeys: Adventure Travel in a Modern Age.* Austin: University of Texas Press, 1995.

Permissions

Chatwin, Bruce. *Anatomy of Restlessness*, Jacket Design by Foos Roundtree, Jacket Photograph by Snowden. Reproduced with permission of Viking Penguin, a division of Penguin Books (USA) Inc. (Copyright 1996).

Stilgoe, John. *Alongshore*. Reproduced with permission of Yale University Press. (Copyright 1994).

Tuan, Yi-Fu. *Escapism*. pp. xi. 1998 (Copyright Holder). Reprinted with permission of The Johns Hopkins University Press.

Zurick, David. *Errant Journeys: Adventure Travel in a Modern Age*. (Copyright 1995). Reproduced with permission of the University of Texas Press.

"Between Geography and Philosophy: What Does it Mean to Be in the Place-World?" By Edward S. Casey. Reproduced with permission from Edward S. Casey. Originally published in the *Annals of the Association of American Geographers*. (December 2001).

"Imperial Bedroom." By Jonathan Franzen. Reproduced with permission from Jonathan Franzen. Originally published in *The New Yorker*. (12 October 1998).

"Mexicans' Ancient Tradition of Honoring Their Ancestors." "By Howard LaFranchi. Copyright, *The Christian Science Monitor* (www.csmonitor.com). Reproduced with permission." (20 November 1996).

"Sleeping with Spuds" was originally published in *Puckerbrush Review* (summer/fall 1997).

"The American Geographies." By Barry Lopez. Reproduced with permission from Barry Lopez. Originally published as *About This Life*. (Copyright 1998, Alfred A. Knopf, Inc.).

Many of these essays were originally published in *The Downeast Coastal Press*.

About the Author

Raised in New Jersey and Steuben, Maine, ALLAN LOCKYER is a 1969 graduate of Sumner Memorial High School in East Sullivan, Maine. He received his bachelor's degree from Southern Arkansas University, master's from Western Kentucky University, and doctorate from the University of Northern Colorado, where he wrote his dissertation on *The Survival of Country Stores in Eastern Maine*. His teaching career began in the summer of 1977 when he was offered a contract to teach one course in geography at the University of Southern Maine. From there he went on to a high school teaching job in Jackson, Mississippi. He taught at Livingstone College in Salisbury, North Carolina from 1978-1982, where he was awarded a United Negro College Fund Faculty Fellowship in order to pursue his doctorate. He taught at Valley City State University in North Dakota until 1986, before joining the faculty at Francis Marion University in Florence, South Carolina, where he is now professor and coordinator of the geography program. His first book, *Clamdiggers and Downeast Country Stores: Eastern Maine's Vanishing Culture*, placed sixth on the Maine Writers and Publishers Bestseller List in 1994.